Master the Manual

A Study Guide to Accompany the
ACE Advanced Health & Fitness Specialist Manual

D1364527

4851 Paramount Drive, San Diego, California 92123, 800-825-3636, www.acefitness.org

Library of Congress Catalog Card Number: 2008933559

ISBN 978-1-890720-28-5

A B C D

Distributed by:
American Council on Exercise
P.O. Box 910449
San Diego, CA 92191-0449
858-279-8227
858-279-8064 (FAX)
800-825-3636
www.acefitness.org

Author: Sabrena Merrill, M.S.
Project Editor: Daniel J. Green
Technical Editor: Cedric X. Bryant, Ph.D.
Design: Karen McGuire
Production Manager: Nancy Garcia

Table of Contents

How to Use This Study Guide

Welcome to *Master the Manual,* a study guide designed as a companion to the *ACE Advanced Health & Fitness Specialist Manual.* The exercises in this book were developed to help you master complex material by breaking it into manageable concepts that you can apply to real-life situations.

Each chapter of the study guide is divided into sections. **Getting Started** introduces you to the material, providing objectives to concentrate on as you read the corresponding chapter in the manual. **Expand Your Knowledge** will test your comprehension through a variety of exercises and drills. **Show What You Know** exercises your ability to apply what you have learned to real-life situations. Some chapters will take you one step further, providing activities to expand your skills in **Practice What You Know**. If you are using the *ACE Advanced Health & Fitness Specialist Manual* in conjunction with this study guide to prepare for the ACE Advanced Health & Fitness Specialist Examination, you should focus not only on learning the concepts, but also on applying them to practical situations. The application of knowledge will best assist you not only in preparing for the examination, but also in working with clients. Follow these steps to get the most from *Master the Manual.*

Step One: Read

Read the student objectives for each chapter, and then read the corresponding chapter in the *ACE Advanced Health & Fitness Specialist Manual*. Read one chapter at a time rather than attempting to read the entire manual at once. As you read, make note of the vocabulary words that are boldface in each manual chapter. When you come across one, be sure that you understand its meaning.

Step Two: Define

After you have read each chapter and noted the boldface words and terms, define each one on a separate piece of paper. Write the definition even if you feel you already know it. Learning is a sensory experience, so the more senses you can involve in the learning process, the more you will be able to retain. Writing down definitions or putting your thoughts into words will help you remember the material more clearly.

Step Three: Exercises

After defining the vocabulary words, skim through the chapter in the manual again. Attempt to do the exercises in the study guide without looking at the manual. Please use a separate piece of paper for additional writing space as needed. Check your answers against the key that appears in Appendix B, which begins on page 194. If you answer a question incorrectly, go back to the text and find out why your answer is wrong. Make a note to yourself for future reference. If you correctly answered a question but feel you were guessing, go back to the manual and read that section again. Do not assume you will remember it.

Step Four: Final Notes

Now is the time to go back to the objectives on the first page of each study guide chapter. Mark any areas you are unsure of or want to learn more about, and reread the related section in the manual. Use the references and suggested reading lists at the end of each manual chapter to find sources for more information.

> The focus of this workbook is on learning and retention. That is why we do not grade the exercises or relate the results to either a score or to your chance for success on the ACE exam. No textbook or study guide can predict your performance on a certification examination. If you feel you need additional preparations, contact ACE to receive information on ACE exam preparation materials and training programs.

CHAPTER 1

Role and Scope of Practice for the Advanced Health & Fitness Specialist

Getting Started

This chapter introduces the role of the ACE-AHFS within the healthcare community and provides guidelines for staying within the defined scope of practice. Standards of care as they pertain to fitness assessment and programming are also discussed. This chapter also covers safety concerns related to program implementation, as well as consultation and privacy issues. After completing this section, you will have a better understanding of:

- The physician-critical pathway
- Different types of disease prevention
- How to use the PAR-Q, PARmed-X, and other health-history forms
- Risk management
- How to build business relationships

Reading Assignment

Read Chapter 1 of the *ACE Advanced Health & Fitness Specialist Manual,* paying special attention to the boldface terms in the chapter. After you have read the chapter, define the boldface terms on a separate piece of paper.

Expand Your Knowledge

I. *List five population groups that are well-suited for the services provided by the ACE Advanced Health & Fitness Specialist (ACE-AHFS).*

1._____

2._____

3._____

4._____

5._____

II. *Fill in the blanks.*

a. Within the healthcare continuum, a _____ may be thought of as a "gatekeeper" who directs the overall healthcare of a client.

b. A personal physician spends approximately _____ with a patient during a typical office visit.

c. _____ prevention is considered the most cost-effective form of healthcare because it helps reduce the costs associated with disease.

d. Using drugs, nutritional supplements, or other natural substances to prevent future disease is called _____.

e. A _____ is any substance other than food that is intended to affect the structure or function of the body.

f. The _____ is a screening tool that may be used by physicians with patients who have given positive responses to the PAR-Q.

g. Patients with _____ contraindications for exercise will either be precluded from exercise or will be referred to a clinical exercise program.

h. In addition to having a new client read an informed consent, the ACE-AHFS should also _____ the document's content areas before the client signs it.

III. *List four accepted reporting structures that can be used by the ACE-AHFS to communicate with a client's referring physician or healthcare team.*

1._____

2._____

3._____

4._____

IV. Fill in the space to the left of each letter by writing (PHYS) if it describes a physiological change, (PERF) if it describes a performance change, or (PSYC) if it describes a psychosocial change related to a client's overall condition.

_____ a. A client complains of difficulty breathing during his typical treadmill warm-up.

_____ b. A client's glucose meter indicates an unusually high level of blood glucose prior to the exercise session.

_____ c. During a seated row exercise, a client reports a tingling numbness in her hand.

_____ d. After a typical circuit-training workout, a client sweats profusely and complains of lightheadedness.

_____ e. For the third time in a row, a client calls at the last minute to cancel his morning appointment.

_____ f. For the first time, a client reports low-back pain while performing a curl-up exercise that has been part of his regular program for the past six weeks.

_____ g. A typically cheerful client walks in for her exercise session appearing fatigued and melancholy.

_____ h. A client requests to lift lighter-than-normal loads for several sessions due to feelings of overall weakness.

V. List seven ways an ACE-AHFS can develop business relationships through self-promotion.

1._____

2._____

3._____

4._____

5._____

6._____

7._____

Show What You Know

Your new client, Marcia, has scheduled to meet with you for two days per week for the next three months for resistance training and flexibility exercise. Marcia was recently released from a physical therapy program to rehabilitate her knee after ACL repair surgery. She has been cleared by her physician for a program of strength training and cardiorespiratory endurance exercise. Since Marcia can meet with you only twice per week, how would you encourage her to fulfill the recommended exercise frequency of three to five days per week?

_____

_____

_____

_____

_____

_____

CHAPTER 2

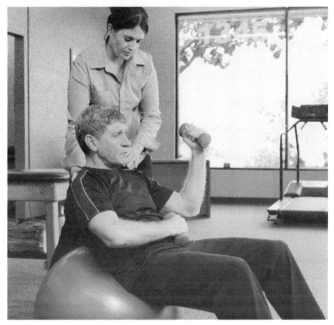

Working With Clients
With Health Challenges

Getting Started

This chapter introduces the concept of working with individuals with various health challenges. It begins with a discussion of the psychological impact of health challenges, and includes sections on empathy and motivation. This chapter also features extensive coverage of lifestyle choices and their impact on physiological capacity. Finally, this chapter provides communication strategies for working with allied healthcare professionals. After completing this section, you will have a better understanding of:

- The ways in which disease, stress, and exercise each impact a client's psychological health
- The importance of empathy
- How various lifestyle choices impact physiological capacity, including tobacco use, food choices, exercise, and performance-enhancing supplements
- The role of the ACE-AHFS on a client's healthcare team

Reading Assignment

Read Chapter 2 of the *ACE Advanced Health & Fitness Specialist Manual*, paying special attention to the boldface terms in the chapter. After you have read the chapter, define the boldface terms on a separate piece of paper.

Expand Your Knowledge

I. *Answer the following questions about working with clients with health challenges.*

    a. A client with a newly-diagnosed health condition schedules her first meeting with an ACE-AHFS. Which topic areas should the ACE-AHFS include in a frank discussion to develop rapport and help the client cope with the unique challenges presented by her condition?

_____

_____

_____

_____

    b. Describe three ways in which a program of consistent physical activity positively impacts a person's psychological profile.

_____

_____

_____

_____

_____

    c. Explain the difference between empathy and sympathy.

_____

_____

_____

_____

_____

d. Give examples of the typical costs associated with starting a new exercise program for a person with health challenges.

    1. Physical:

_____

_____

_____

    2. Mental:

_____

_____

_____

    3. Emotional:

_____

_____

_____

    4. Monetary:

_____

_____

_____

_____

II. *Fill in the space to the left of each letter by writing (EX) if it describes an external stressor or (IN) if it describes an internal stressor.*

_____a. Direct sunlight streaming into a circuit-training area

_____b. Consuming three cups of coffee prior to a workout session

_____c. An impending deadline for completion of a work project

_____d. The birth of a couple's third child

_____e. An unpleasant encounter with a driver on the way to the gym

_____f. An expectation that exercise should bring rapid results

_____g. Irritation about not performing an exercise perfectly on the first try

_____h. Taking a new job that requires more hours per week than expected

_____i. Moving from a residential home into an assisted-living community

_____j. Making funeral arrangements after the death of a spouse

III. *List and describe four steps related to the development of stress-coping skills.*

1._____

_____

_____

2._____

_____

_____

3._____

_____

_____

4._____

_____

_____

IV. List six keys to effective empathy.

1._____

2._____

3._____

4._____

5._____

6._____

V. Describe the potential negative impacts of both alcohol and caffeine on a client's overall health.

Alcohol:

_____

_____

_____

_____

Caffeine:

_____

_____

_____

_____

VI. Explain how each of the following components of a client's intake information and history may be approached by the ACE-AHFS.

1. Chief complaint/primary goal:

_____

_____

_____

_____

2. History of present illness or injury:

_____

_____

_____

_____

3. Medical history/exercise history:

_____

_____

_____

_____

4. Allergies and medications:

_____

_____

_____

_____

5. Family and social history/support network:

_____

_____

_____

_____

6. Review of systems:

_____

_____

_____

_____

7. Physical exam/initial evaluation:

_____

_____

_____

_____

8. Assessment:

_____

_____

_____

_____

9. Plan:

_____

_____

_____

_____

Show What You Know

Bob was recently diagnosed with mild hypertension and is interested in beginning a lifestyle-modification program at the recommendation of his physician. Bob has been cleared for low-intensity aerobic exercise and circuit training with light resistance. During his initial interview, Bob reveals that he has a high level of anxiety about his diagnosis and fears that his life will now revolve around his disease. As an ACE-AHFS, how would you deal with Bob's anxiety and fear during your exercise sessions?

_____

_____

_____

_____

_____

_____

_____

CHAPTER 3

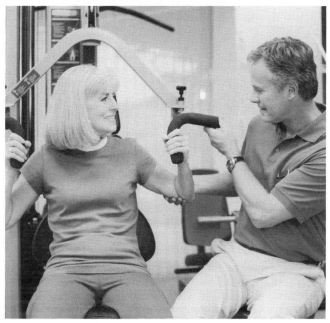

Communication Strategies
and Behavior Change

Getting Started

This chapter begins by focusing on the importance of developing rapport with each new client by using effective communication techniques. Various principles of behavior change are discussed, along with concepts of motivation and adherence. Strategies for behavior change are also presented, including setting SMART goals and focusing on exercise-specific self-efficacy. After completing this section, you will have a better understanding of:
- Principles of behavior change, including operant conditioning and stress and negative emotions
- The health belief model, the protection motivation theory, and the transtheoretical model of behavior change
- Learning models, including cognitive learning and motor learning
- Psychological issues related to illness and injury

Reading Assignment

Read Chapter 3 of the *ACE Advanced Health & Fitness Specialist Manual,* paying special attention to the boldface terms in the chapter. After you have read the chapter, define the boldface terms on a separate piece of paper.

Expand Your Knowledge

I. *Match each term with its associated descriptive statement.*

_____ a. The stage of behavior change in which a person is not
currently active, but is intending to become more active
some day

_____ b. Variables or factors that occur after a person's actions

_____ c. A sense of being controlled by outside factors

_____ d. The extent to which a person follows, or sticks with, an
exercise program

_____ e. The development of mutual understanding and trust in a
relationship

_____ f. Variables or factors that precede and influence a person's
actions

_____ g. The stage of behavior change in which a person is plan-
ning to increase his or her physical-activity level soon and is
taking steps to get ready

_____ h. The concept of motivation that suggests that people need
to feel competent, autonomous, and connected to others

_____ i. Theory of behavior change that suggests that a person's
health beliefs influence decisions about behavior change

_____ j. A strong sense of being in control as a result of one's own
efforts and abilities

1. Self-determination theory
2. Antecedents
3. Internal locus of control
4. Preparation
5. Consequences
6. External locus of control
7. Contemplation
8. Health belief model
9. Rapport
10. Adherence

II. *How should the ACE-AHFS deal with each of the following potential barriers to effective client
communication?*

1. Cultural differences:

_____

_____

_____

2. Emotional health problems:

_____

_____

_____

3. Too little/too much explanation:

_____

_____

_____

4. Stress/feeling rushed:

_____

_____

_____

5. Fitness center environment:

_____

_____

_____

III. *Describe common characteristics of individuals within each stage of the transtheoretical model of behavior change, and then list tactics the ACE-AHFS can employ to help improve program adherence for clients in each stage.*

1. Precontemplation:

_____

_____

_____

2. Contemplation:

_____

_____

_____

_____

3. Preparation:

_____

_____

_____

_____

4. Action:

_____

_____

_____

_____

5. Maintenance:

_____

_____

_____

_____

IV. List and explain four strategies that can encourage clients to find immediate and long-term psychological benefits from their participation in regular physical activity.

1._____

_____

_____

2._____

_____

_____

3._____

_____

_____

4._____

_____

_____

V. Fill in the blanks.

 a. A psychological state in which a person believes that he or she is helpless, or has no power or control over certain situations, is called _____ .

 b. People who exercise to achieve a reward, such as a T-shirt or the praise of a family member, are said to be _____ , whereas people who exercise because they enjoy competition or because exercising feels good, are said to be _____ .

 c. In the operant conditioning model of behavior change, exercise participation, or a lack of participation, is viewed as part of a _____ , both preceded and followed by factors that influence whether or not a client participates in physical activity.

 d. _____ refers to a person's situation- or behavior-specific confidence that he or she can perform a given task.

 e. The process of acquiring and improving motor skills is called _____ .

 f. For a client dealing with health challenges, his or her _____ of the illness or injury may be more important than the actual physical nature of the illness or injury.

 g. It is estimated that depression effects approximately _____ of individuals receiving medical treatment.

 h. Clients with health challenges who are fearful that exercise may cause them harm should be given low levels of exercise initially to strengthen confidence and improve _____ .

VI. List five strategies for effective motor learning.

1._____

2._____

3._____

4._____

5._____

Show What You Know

Yesterday, you met and interviewed your new client, Cindy. As you are preparing your assessment plan and program design for Cindy, you recall that she reflected in the interview about starting many fitness programs in the past and failing to stick with them over and over again. You are concerned that Cindy may feel a lack of control when it comes to taking charge of her health. How would help Cindy move past her associations with failure so that she can successfully reach her fitness goals?

_____

_____

_____

_____

_____

_____

_____

_____

CHAPTER 4

Professional Relationships and Business Strategies

Getting Started

This chapter covers communicating and networking with allied healthcare professionals, as well as several important business strategies. Topics include SOAP notes and other forms of standardized communication, billing and payment policies, and legal issues and professional responsibilities. After completing this section, you will have a better understanding of:
- Various barriers to effective communication and how to overcome them
- How to develop a thorough business plan
- Confidentiality issues and how to manage them in your daily interactions with clients and coworkers
- How to market your business and attain referrals

Reading Assignment

Read Chapter 4 of the *ACE Advanced Health & Fitness Specialist Manual,* paying special attention to the boldface terms in the chapter. After you have read the chapter, define the boldface terms on a separate piece of paper.

Expand Your Knowledge

I. List eight objectives for communication between the ACE-AHFS and a client's allied healthcare team.

1._____

2._____

3._____

4._____

5._____

6._____

7._____

8._____

II. List 10 documents that should be included and maintained in a complete client folder.

1._____

2._____

3._____

4._____

5._____

6._____

7._____

8._____

9._____

10._____

III. Describe each component of the SOAP note.

    1. Subjective:

    _____

    _____

    _____

    2. Objective:

    _____

    _____

    _____

    3. Assessment:

    _____

    _____

    _____

    4. Plan:

    _____

    _____

    _____

    _____

    _____

    _____

    _____

IV. List four potential barriers to communication between an ACE-AHFS and the client's healthcare team, and then provide strategies the ACE-AHFS can use to overcome them.

1._____

_____

_____

2._____

_____

_____

3._____

_____

_____

4._____

_____

_____

V. Fill in the blanks.

a. To protect a client's private health information, all client files should be stamped with
"_____" or "_____."

b. All computer-based client information should be _____ protected.

c. _____ is defined as a group of activities designed to expedite transactions by creating, distributing, pricing, and promoting goods, services, and ideas.

d. The way a business and/or individual tries to get consumers to purchase products and services over those offered by the competition is called _____.

e. _____ is the most inexpensive form of marketing.

f. It has been noted that a typical dissatisfied customer will tell _____ people about his problem, and one in five will tell _____.

g. Two very important factors to consider in receiving on-time payment for services from clients are _____ and _____.

h. The ACE-AHFS provides a safe and effective bridge for the patient to cross from the structured clinical treatment and/or rehabilitation environment to _____ or _____ exercise.

VI. List six ways that an ACE-AHFS can protect him- or herself from legal problems.

1.＿＿＿＿＿＿＿＿＿＿＿＿＿＿＿＿＿＿＿＿＿＿＿＿＿＿＿＿＿＿＿

2.＿＿＿＿＿＿＿＿＿＿＿＿＿＿＿＿＿＿＿＿＿＿＿＿＿＿＿＿＿＿＿

3.＿＿＿＿＿＿＿＿＿＿＿＿＿＿＿＿＿＿＿＿＿＿＿＿＿＿＿＿＿＿＿

4.＿＿＿＿＿＿＿＿＿＿＿＿＿＿＿＿＿＿＿＿＿＿＿＿＿＿＿＿＿＿＿

5.＿＿＿＿＿＿＿＿＿＿＿＿＿＿＿＿＿＿＿＿＿＿＿＿＿＿＿＿＿＿＿

6.＿＿＿＿＿＿＿＿＿＿＿＿＿＿＿＿＿＿＿＿＿＿＿＿＿＿＿＿＿＿＿

VII. List and describe the three major options for forming a business entity.

1.＿＿＿＿＿＿＿＿＿＿＿＿＿＿＿＿＿＿＿＿＿＿＿＿＿＿＿＿＿＿＿

＿＿＿＿＿＿＿＿＿＿＿＿＿＿＿＿＿＿＿＿＿＿＿＿＿＿＿＿＿＿＿＿

＿＿＿＿＿＿＿＿＿＿＿＿＿＿＿＿＿＿＿＿＿＿＿＿＿＿＿＿＿＿＿＿

2.＿＿＿＿＿＿＿＿＿＿＿＿＿＿＿＿＿＿＿＿＿＿＿＿＿＿＿＿＿＿＿

＿＿＿＿＿＿＿＿＿＿＿＿＿＿＿＿＿＿＿＿＿＿＿＿＿＿＿＿＿＿＿＿

＿＿＿＿＿＿＿＿＿＿＿＿＿＿＿＿＿＿＿＿＿＿＿＿＿＿＿＿＿＿＿＿

3.＿＿＿＿＿＿＿＿＿＿＿＿＿＿＿＿＿＿＿＿＿＿＿＿＿＿＿＿＿＿＿

＿＿＿＿＿＿＿＿＿＿＿＿＿＿＿＿＿＿＿＿＿＿＿＿＿＿＿＿＿＿＿＿

＿＿＿＿＿＿＿＿＿＿＿＿＿＿＿＿＿＿＿＿＿＿＿＿＿＿＿＿＿＿＿＿

Show What You Know

Read the following example and write a SOAP note for the client.

During your initial consultation with a prospective client, Mary Mason, you determine that your services can help her reach her stated goals. Through the interview process you discover that Mary is a 52-year-old executive business manager with a very hectic work schedule who has recently been diagnosed with hypertension. From the encouragement of her physician, she has enlisted your services to help her lower her blood pressure, alleviate stress, lose 30 pounds (14 kg), and feel better. Taking into account her busy work schedule and social life, she will be able to commit to only three workout sessions a week, but she is willing to walk to and from work (approximately 15 minutes each way) at least twice per week. Mary's initial assessment results reveal that she weighs 165 pounds (74 kg) and has 28% body fat.

Nutritional Considerations
for an Active Lifestyle

Getting Started

This chapter defines what types of nutritional advice fall within the scope of practice for an ACE-AHFS. In addition, it covers the requirements and recommendations for specific micro- and macronutrients. Nutrition and hydration for optimal performance are also discussed, as are various eating and exercise (body-image) disorders. After completing this section, you will have a better understanding of:

- Absorption, digestion, and utilization of macronutrients and their effect on exercise performance
- Nutrition, exercise, and weight control
- Hydration, water balance, and gastric emptying
- The various types of vegetarianism and how they affect exercise performance

Reading Assignment

Read Chapter 5 of the *ACE Advanced Health & Fitness Specialist Manual,* paying special attention to the boldface terms in the chapter. After you have read the chapter, define the boldface terms on a separate piece of paper.

Expand Your Knowledge

I. Describe the major differences between the following pairs of words or phrases.

1. vitamins and minerals

_____

_____

_____

2. water-soluble vitamins and fat-soluble vitamins

_____

_____

_____

3. monosaccharide and oligosaccharide

_____

_____

_____

4. nonessential amino acids and essential amino acids

_____

_____

_____

5. mechanical digestion and chemical digestion

_____

_____

_____

6. esophageal sphincter and pyloric sphincter

_____

_____

_____

7. positive energy balance and negative energy balance

_____

_____

_____

II. *List six general recommendations made by the MyPyramid Food Guidance System regarding the types of food to consume.*

1._____

_____

_____

2._____

_____

_____

3._____

_____

_____

4._____

_____

_____

5._____

_____

_____

6._____

_____

_____

III. Answer the following questions about carbohydrate.

1. List the daily recommended intakes of carbohydrates for average adults and children, pregnant women, lactating women, and athletes.

_____

_____

_____

2. Explain how adequate consumption of dietary fiber (both soluble and insoluble) may improve health.

_____

_____

_____

_____

3. Describe the glycemic index (GI) and explain how it may be used to improve both performance and health.

_____

_____

_____

_____

IV. Answer the following questions about fat.

    1. List the primary functions that fats serve in the body.

\
\
\

    2. Define eicosanoids and their relationship to omega-3 and omega-6 fatty acids.

\
\
\

    3. Describe the functions of omega-3 and omega-6 fatty acids and the importance of maintaining a balance between the two substances.

\
\
\

    4. Describe the harmful effects of trans fat and explain how an ACE-AHFS can encourage clients to avoid them.

\
\
\

V. Answer the following questions about protein.

1. List the recommended daily intakes for protein for average individuals, endurance athletes, and strength athletes.

_____

_____

_____

_____

2. List the primary functions of protein in the body.

_____

_____

_____

_____

3. List and describe the three factors that affect a specific protein source's biological value.

_____

_____

_____

_____

VI. Match the digestion-related term with its associated descriptive statement.

_____a. A wave-like motion in the esophagus that serves to push food to the stomach

_____b. The term for food that has made it to the small intestine in the process of digestion

_____c. The enzyme-rich liquid involved in the first step of chemical digestion

_____d. Provides a surface on which the absorption of nutrients occurs in the small intestine

_____e. The structure in the throat responsible for preventing a bolus from entering the trachea

_____f. The gateway through which waste and fiber pass from the small intestine to the large intestine

_____g. The organ that acts to detoxify harmful substances before they are circulated throughout the body

_____h. The long, hollow tube that runs from the mouth to the anus where digestion and absorption occur

1. Epiglottis
2. Brush border
3. Ileocecal valve
4. Liver
5. Chyme
6. Gastrointestinal tract
7. Peristalsis
8. Saliva

VII. Describe how the sympathetic nervous system and its associated hormones function to prepare the body for exercise.

_____

_____

_____

_____

_____

_____

_____

VIII. Fill in the blanks.

a. Creatine is the primary energy source in the _____ system.

b. ADP combines with a phosphate from stored creatine phosphate to produce _____ and _____.

c. _____ is a metabolic end product that upon accumulation causes muscle burn and decreased blood pH.

d. The process by which energy from electrons that have passed through the electron transport chain are captured and stored to produce ATP is called _____.

e. When the body attempts to compensate for lack of water by retaining more water and excreting more concentrated urine, it is in a state of _____.

f. The condition in which the body experiences low sodium levels due to ingesting excessive amounts of water is called _____.

g. _____ is the passage of food and fluid from the stomach to the small intestine for further digestion and absorption.

h. In general, the ACE-AHFS should advise clients to eat about _____ before exercise to give their system a chance to move the food out of the stomach and begin digestion and absorption.

i. For refueling purposes, the American Dietetic Association (ADA) recommends a carbohydrate intake of _____ in the first 30 minutes after exercise and then every _____ for four to six hours.

IX. List and briefly describe the USA Track and Field guidelines for optimal hydration during exercise.

1._____

_____

_____

2._____

_____

_____

3._____

_____

_____

4._____

_____

_____

5._____

_____

_____

X. Complete the third column in the table by filling in the ways in which the factors listed in the first column influence resting metabolic rate (RMR).

Factors Affecting Resting Metabolic Rate

Factor	RMR	Comments
Age	↓	
Body Temperature	↑	
Caffeine and Tobacco	↑	
Gender	↑↓	
Nervous System Activity	↑	
Nutritional Status	↓	
Pregnancy	↑	
Thyroid Hormones	↑↓	

Note: ↑ = Increase;   ↓ = Decrease;   ↑↓ = Variable

Source: Modified from Wardlaw, G.M., Hampl, J.S., & DiSilvestro, R.A. (2004). *Perspectives in Nutrition* (6th ed.). New York: McGraw-Hill.

XI. List nine strategies that an ACE-AHFS can use to help prevent eating and exercise disorders in high-risk clients.

1._____

_____

2._____

_____

3._____

_____

4._____

_____

5._____

_____

6._____

_____

7._____

_____

8._____

_____

9._____

_____

Practice What You Know

I. *Practice performing the Mifflin-St. Jeor equation to determine resting metabolic rate for you and for various clients.*

II. *Visit www.MyPyramid.gov, complete the registration process, and track your physical activity and nutrient intake for several days. Use your experience navigating the website to educate your clients about the interactive features that may be useful for them.*

CHAPTER 6

Coronary Artery Disease

Getting Started

This chapter offers a thorough examination of coronary artery disease (CAD), including the principal diagnostic tests for CAD and exercise recommendations for the various manifestations of the disease. This chapter also makes the important distinction between stable and unstable CAD and defines the types of clients with whom it is appropriate for the ACE-AHFS to work. After completing this section, you will have a better understanding of:

- The various types of diagnostics tests that are used to identify CAD
- What types of fitness assessments are appropriate for these clients
- The essential exercise recommendations for clients with stable CAD, including time, intensity, and progression
- Post–coronary artery bypass grafting and percutaneous transluminal coronary angioplasty intervention

Reading Assignment

Read Chapter 6 of the *ACE Advanced Health & Fitness Specialist Manual,* paying special attention to the boldface terms and the case study at the back of the chapter. After you have read the chapter, define the boldface terms on a separate piece of paper.

Expand Your Knowledge

I. Describe the major differences between the following pairs of words or phrases.

1. Phase I cardiac rehabilitation and phase II cardiac rehabilitation

_____

_____

_____

2. Atherosclerosis and atherogenesis

_____

_____

_____

3. Stable angina and unstable angina

_____

_____

_____

II. Briefly describe the following diagnostic tests for coronary artery disease (CAD).

1. Electrocardiogram (ECG) exercise test

_____

_____

_____

2. Radionuclide stress test

_____

_____

_____

3. Stress echocardiography

_____

_____

_____

4. Coronary angiography

_____

_____

_____

5. Coronary computed tomography (CT) angiography

_____

_____

_____

6. High-resolution cardiovascular magnetic resonance imaging (CMRI)

_____

_____

_____

7. Intravascular ultrasound (IVUS)

_____

_____

_____

8. Coronary calcium scoring

_____

_____

_____

9. B-mode ultrasound assessment

_____

_____

_____

III. List seven major benefits of exercise training for clients with CAD.

1._____

2._____

3._____

4._____

5._____

6._____

7._____

IV. Describe the essential exercise guidelines for clients with stable angina.

_____

_____

_____

_____

_____

_____

V. Explain the typical self-administer protocol for clients experiencing angina pectoris who have been pre-scribed nitroglycerin PRN.

_____

_____

_____

_____

_____

_____

_____

_____

VI. List the common symptoms associated with the following cardiac conditions.

1. Cardiac dysrhythmias

_____

_____

_____

2. Myocardial infarction (MI)

_____

_____

_____

_____

_____

_____

3. Restenosis following PTCA or CABG

_____

_____

_____

VII. Answer the following questions regarding essential exercise recommendations for a client with stable CAD.

1. What is the optimal weekly energy expenditure for the improvement of CAD risk factors?

_____

_____

_____

2. Describe ACSM's recommendations for the initial, improvement, and maintenance stages of aerobic exercise program development for clients with stable CAD.

_____

_____

_____

3. Define "double product" and describe exercise activities that are known to increase it.

_____

_____

_____

4. List the American Heart Association's recommendations for the initial resistance-training program for individuals with and without cardiovascular disease.

_____

_____

_____

_____

_____

_____

5. Explain how yogic breathing may be beneficial for clients with CAD.

_____

_____

_____

_____

Show What You Know

What general exercise recommendations would you give for the following client?

Fred is a 71-year-old retired salesman who recently experienced a severe angina episode while shoveling snow in his driveway. Shortly after his arrival at the hospital, a cardiac catheterization revealed triple-vessel disease and further testing found that he had an ejection fraction of 25%. He underwent coronary artery bypass grafting (CABG) and was referred to cardiac rehabilitation. After being released from phase II cardiac rehabilitation, Fred is ready to continue exercising in a community-based program. He has been cleared for exercise and is currently showing stable ventricular function and is asymptomatic.

_____

_____

_____

_____

_____

_____

_____

_____

CHAPTER 7

Blood Lipid Disorders

Getting Started

This chapter explains the various types of blood lipid disorders and helps the ACE-AHFS categorize potential clients according to the latest National Cholesterol Education Program (NCEP) guidelines. The lipid/lipoprotein response to exercise is also discussed, along with the essential exercise-programming steps for individuals with dyslipidemia. After completing this section, you will have a better understanding of:

- The various types of lipoproteins, including LDL, HDL, VLDL, and non-HDL
- Medications used to treat dyslipidemia and their effects on the body's response to exercise
- How to program the appropriate volume of exercise to help individuals manage their blood lipid profiles
- The 10 essential exercise-programming steps for individuals with dyslipidemia, beginning with evaluating their health and lifestyle histories and ending with partnering with appropriate healthcare professionals

Reading Assignment

Read Chapter 7 of the *ACE Advanced Health & Fitness Specialist Manual*, paying special attention to the boldface terms and the case study at the back of the chapter. After you have read the chapter, define the boldface terms on a separate piece of paper.

Expand Your Knowledge

I.   *Fill in the space to the left of each letter by placing (VLDL) if the statement describes very-low-density lipoprotein, (LDL) if it describes low-density lipoprotein, (HDL) if it describes high-density lipoprotein, or (NHDL) if it describes non-HDL.*

_____a. Directly correlated with the risk for coronary heart disease

_____b. A good marker for apoprotein B

_____c. Inversely correlated with coronary heart disease

_____d. Contains 60–70% of the body's total serum cholesterol

_____e. Contains 10–15% of the body's total serum cholesterol

_____f. The primary focus of most blood-lipid-lowering therapies

_____g. Responds well to dietary and physical-activity changes, especially in children

_____h. Strongly associated with obesity, the metabolic syndrome, and type 2 diabetes

_____i. Important in reverse cholesterol transport

_____j. The most significant blood lipid involved in the development of atherosclerosis

_____k. A major carrier of triglycerides in the plasma

II. *List the quantitative values for classification of LDL cholesterol, total cholesterol, HDL cholesterol, and triglycerides as set forth by the Third Report of the Expert Panel on Detection, Evaluation, and Treatment of High Blood Cholesterol in Adults (ATP III).*

LDL Cholesterol	mg/dL
Optimal	
Near optimal/above optimal	
Borderline high	
High	
Very high	
Total Cholesterol	
Desirable	
Borderline high	
High	
HDL Cholesterol	
Low	
High	
Triglycerides	
Normal	
Borderline high	
High	
Very high	

III. Give a brief description of each level of the Framingham coronary heart disease (CHD) risk classification and its associated ATP III LDL-cholesterol goals and cutpoints.

  1. High and very high risk

_____

_____

_____

_____

_____

_____

  2. Moderately high risk

_____

_____

_____

_____

  3. Low risk

_____

_____

_____

_____

IV. Answer the following questions about the metabolic syndrome and dyslipidemia.

   1. List the core metabolic risk factors associated with the metabolic syndrome.

_____

_____

_____

_____

_____

   2. What are the root causes of the metabolic syndrome?

_____

_____

_____

_____

_____

   3. Briefly describe "cardiometabolic risk."

_____

_____

_____

_____

_____

   4. List seven FDA-approved medications for dyslipidemia and briefly explain how each type acts to improve blood lipids.

_____

_____

_____

_____

_____

_____

_____

_____

_____

_____

_____

V. Fill in the blanks.

a. Blood triglycerides generally decrease immediately after a session of _____ and remain lower for up to _____ after the session.

b. Decreased body fat correlates well with reduced _____ cholesterol and increased _____ cholesterol.

c. Compared to other lipids, elevated _____ are generally more responsive to exercise training.

d. Most research indicates a minimal exercise-training threshold of _____ kcal per week, and an ideal volume of _____ kcal per week or more, to produce reductions in LDL and total cholesterol.

e. After consuming a meal, a person's blood fat, particularly triglyceride, response is called _____.

f. Prolonged elevated postprandial triglycerides above 250 to 300 mg/dL may result in _____, _____, and _____.

g. ACSM recommends the following exercise guidelines for persons with dyslipidemia:
- Primary activity: _____
- Intensity: _____
- Frequency: _____
- Duration: _____

h. For blood lipid changes or weight loss to occur, a client's minimal weekly energy expenditure would be equivalent to about _____ or more walking step counts beyond the client's weekly baseline step count.

VI. Complete the table by filling in the recommended gross energy expenditure goals for each of the lipid- and lipoprotein-related conditions.

Elevated LDL and/or total cholesterol	
Low HDL	
Elevated triglycerides	
Combined dyslipidemia	

VII. Briefly explain why it is important for the ACE-AHFS to carefully track and document the musculoskeletal-symptom status of a client with a blood lipid disorder.

_____

_____

_____

_____

_____

_____

_____

_____

Show What You Know

What recommendations would you give the following client regarding an exercise program to aid in attenuating her condition?

After many failed attempts at controlling her high cholesterol and overweight through diet alone, Lucy, a 58-year-old seamstress, is ready to incorporate lovastatin and a program of physical activity at the recommendation of her physician. She has purchased a pedometer and is ready to begin her exercise program.

_____

_____

_____

_____

_____

_____

_____

_____

_____

CHAPTER 8

Hypertension

Getting Started

This chapter discusses the epidemiology and diagnostic criteria for hypertension, in addition to explaining the various treatment options for individuals with hypertension. The role of exercise in treating this disorder is a primary focus, along with the cardiovascular responses to exercise. Finally, training guidelines are provided that cover cardiovascular, resistance, and mind-body exercise. After completing this section, you will have a better understanding of:

- The various hypertensive medications that these clients may be taking, along with how each affects the body's response to exercise
- The National Heart, Lung, and Blood Institute's guidelines for hypertensive clients
- How hypertension is treated, including pharmacological, non-pharmacological, surgical, and exercise treatment
- The relationship between hypertension and thermoregulation

Reading Assignment

Read Chapter 8 of the *ACE Advanced Health & Fitness Specialist Manual,* paying special attention to the boldface terms and the case studies at the back of the chapter. After you have read the chapter, define the boldface terms on a separate piece of paper.

Expand Your Knowledge

I. Describe the relationship between the following pairs of words or word phrases.

1. Advancing age and hypertension

2. Cardiac output and total peripheral resistance

3. Renin-angiotensin-aldosterone system (RAAS) and blood pressure

4. Left-ventricular hypertrophy and hypertension

5. Korotkoff sounds and blood pressure assessment

II. List the five lifestyle modifications to manage hypertension as recommended by *The Seventh Report of the Joint National Committee on Prevention, Detection, Evaluation, and Treatment of High Blood Pressure (JNC 7)*. After each modification, list its associated approximate systolic blood pressure reduction range.

1._____

_____

2._____

_____

3._____

_____

4._____

_____

5._____

_____

III. Briefly explain both the acute and chronic effects of exercise on blood pressure.

_____

_____

_____

_____

_____

_____

_____

_____

_____

_____

IV. *List nine types of hypertensive medications and briefly explain how each one acts to reduce high blood pressure.*

1._____

_____

_____

2._____

_____

_____

3._____

_____

_____

4._____

_____

_____

5._____

_____

_____

6._____

_____

_____

7._____

_____

_____

8._____

_____

_____

9._____

_____

_____

V. Fill in the blanks.

a. In general, regular exercise training and greater baseline fitness levels are associated with a _____ incidence of hypertension.

b. The magnitude of resting blood pressure reduction due to aerobic exercise is greatest in _____ individuals.

c. With exercise training, the primary mechanism for the decrease in blood pressure is through _____.

d. Overall, there is a(n) _____ in sympathetic nerve activity with exercise training.

e. Measuring the amount of _____ in the blood is an indirect assessment of sympathetic nervous system activity.

f. As a consequence of regular exercise training, the combined phenomena of _____, _____, _____, and _____ result in decreased vascular resistance and contribute to a reduction in blood pressure.

g. People with hypertension have a _____ ability to dissipate body heat to the environment during heat stress.

h. Most heat-related injuries and deaths occur in individuals with _____.

i. Individuals taking _____ to control hypertension can easily become dehydrated during heat stress.

VI. List the cardiovascular training recommendations for hypertensive clients.

    1. Frequency: _____

    2. Intensity: _____

    3. Time: _____

    4. Type: _____

VII. Briefly describe the applications of resistance training and mind-body exercise in an exercise program for a client with hypertension.

_____

_____

_____

_____

_____

_____

_____

_____

_____

Show What You Know

Jerry, a 59-year-old real estate broker, has recently been diagnosed with hypertension. His physician has cleared him for exercise and has prescribed 75 mg of Atenolol per day. What precautions should Jerry take during exercise considering his recent diagnosis and new medication requirement?

_____

_____

_____

_____

_____

_____

_____

_____

CHAPTER 9

Asthma

Getting Started

This chapter discusses the diagnostic testing and criteria for asthma and offers tips on how clients can avoid common triggers. Exercise and its relationship to asthma are covered in detail, including pulmonary responses to exercise training, and programming and progression guidelines and considerations. After completing this section, you will have a better understanding of:

- Diagnostic testing techniques, including spirometry, peak expiratory flow, and allergy testing
- Asthma treatment and education
- How to manage a client's asthma exacerbation

Reading Assignment

Read Chapter 9 of the *ACE Advanced Health & Fitness Specialist Manual*, paying special attention to the boldface terms and the case studies at the back of the chapter. After you have read the chapter, define the boldface terms on a separate piece of paper.

Expand Your Knowledge

I. Answer the following questions about asthma.

1. Describe the two most significant environmental triggers linked to the development of asthma.

_____

_____

_____

2. Briefly explain the "hygiene hypothesis."

_____

_____

_____

3. List the common physical findings in individuals with asthma.

_____

_____

_____

4. Describe spirometry and explain how it is used to monitor lung function over time.

_____

_____

_____

_____

_____

_____

II. After each asthma trigger, list at least two things a person can do to help prevent an asthma exacerbation.

1. Animal dander

_____

_____

_____

2. Dust mites

_____

_____

_____

3. Cockroaches

_____

_____

_____

4. Indoor mold

_____

_____

_____

5. Pollen and outdoor mold

_____

_____

_____

6. Tobacco smoke

_____

_____

_____

7. Smoke, strong odors, and sprays

_____

_____

_____

8. Vacuum cleaning

_____

_____

_____

III. List and describe the three zones used for monitoring asthma symptoms in conjunction with using a peak flow meter and the precautions individuals should take in each zone.

_____

_____

_____

_____

_____

_____

_____

_____

_____

IV. Briefly describe the difference between long-term-control medications and quick-relief medications for asthma.

_____

_____

_____

_____

_____

_____

_____

_____

_____

V. List five questions the ACE-AHFS should ask a client when he or she discovers a client has asthma.

1._____

_____

_____

2._____

_____

_____

3._____

_____

_____

4._____

_____

_____

5._____

_____

_____

VI. List five actions an ACE-AHFS should take if a client experiences an asthma exacerbation during an exercise session.

1._____

_____

_____

2._____

_____

_____

3._____

_____

_____

4._____

_____

_____

5._____

_____

_____

VII. Match each term with its associated descriptive statement.

_____a. A condition resulting from a loss of heat, water, or both from the lungs during exercise due to hyperventilation of air that is cooler and drier than the air of the respiratory tree

_____b. During exercise, these structures warm and humidify the air entering the respiratory system

_____c. A type of potent long-term-control asthma medication

_____d. An episode of progressively worsening shortness of breath, cough, wheezing, and/or chest tightness that results in decreased expiratory flow

_____e. The total amount of air that can be forcibly exhaled after a maximal inhalation, compared to a predicted value

_____f. Allergic hypersensitivity

_____g. A bronchodilator that opens airways in the lungs

_____h. A pulmonary function test that measures lung function by assessing the volume and flow of air that can be maximally inhaled and exhaled

_____i. The product of the volume of air inspired per breath and ventilatory rate

1. Asthma exacerbation

2. Albuterol

3. Tracheobronchial mucosa

4. Atopy

5. Spirometry

6. Corticosteriod

7. Exercise-induced bronchospasm

8. Forced vital capacity

9. Minute ventilation

VIII. List 11 general physical-activity guidelines for clients with asthma.

1._____

_____

_____

2._____

_____

_____

3._____

_____

_____

4._____

_____

_____

5._____

_____

_____

6._____

_____

_____

7._____

_____

_____

8._____

_____

_____

9._____

_____

_____

10._____

_____

_____

11._____

_____

_____

Show What You Know

During your first exercise session together, your 23-year-old client, Rachel, complains of difficulty breathing and tightness in her chest. She explains that her asthma has been acting up lately, probably due to the high pollen count this season. She also informs you that this is the first time she has had asthma associated with exercise. What recommendations would you give Sarah at this time?

_____

_____

_____

_____

_____

_____

_____

_____

_____

_____

_____

_____

_____

_____

_____

_____

_____

CHAPTER 10

Overweight and Obesity

Getting Started

This chapter offers an overview of the potential causes of overweight and obesity and discusses the biology of obesity, including immune hormones, ghrelin, and the obesity–sleep connection. Special considerations related to overweight and obesity are provided, along with programming and progression guidelines for working with overweight and obese clients. After completing this section, you will have a better understanding of:

- The obesity medications and the physiological response to each
- The role of exercise in weight loss and weight-gain prevention
- Biomechanical considerations specific to this population
- The psychological issues associated with obesity and related dietary patterns
- Surgical interventions for obesity

Reading Assignment

Read Chapter 10 of the *ACE Advanced Health & Fitness Specialist Manual,* paying special attention to the bold-face terms and the case studies at the back of the chapter. After you have read the chapter, define the boldface terms on a separate piece of paper.

Expand Your Knowledge

I. Describe the relationship between the following pairs of words or phrases.

1. Energy balance and obesity

_____

_____

2. Android fat and cardiovascular disease

_____

_____

3. Leptin and adiponectin

_____

_____

_____

_____

_____

4. Cytokines and inflammation

_____

_____

5. Ghrelin and peptide YY

_____

_____

6. Non-exercise activity thermogenesis (NEAT) and body composition

_____

_____

II. *What are the three lifestyle modification components of a successful obesity treatment program as recommended by the National Heart, Lung, and Blood Institute (NHLBI) and the North American Association for the Study of Obesity?*

_____

_____

_____

_____

_____

III. *List seven types of foods that should be included in a healthy eating plan for individuals interested in weight loss.*

1._____

_____

2._____

_____

3._____

_____

4._____

_____

5._____

_____

6._____

_____

7._____

_____

IV. List nine behavioral techniques that can be implemented to help clients attain long-term weight control.

1._____

2._____

3._____

4._____

5._____

6._____

7._____

8._____

9._____

V. List seven chief behavioral characteristics shared by individuals who have achieved and maintained weight loss.

1._____

2._____

3._____

4._____

5._____

6._____

7._____

VI. Describe the "accumulated time" approach to physical activity as a means for weight control.

_____

_____

_____

_____

_____

_____

_____

_____

VII. Explain how the resting metabolic rate (RMR) of muscle tissue contributes to weight management.

_____

_____

_____

_____

_____

_____

_____

_____

VIII. Briefly explain how the obesity medications sibutramine and orlistat act in the body to combat obesity.

_____

_____

_____

_____

_____

_____

_____

_____

_____

_____

_____

_____

_____

_____

_____

_____

_____

_____

_____

_____

_____

_____

_____

_____

_____

IX. *List the 10 exercise guidelines for overweight and obese clients as recommended by the American College of Sports Medicine (ACSM).*

1._____

_____

2._____

_____

3._____

_____

4._____

_____

5._____

_____

6._____

_____

7._____

_____

8._____

_____

9._____

_____

10._____

_____

X. Explain why each of the following exercise modalities would be an appropriate choice for obese clients.

1. Aquatic exercise

_____

_____

2. Recumbent stationary cycling

_____

_____

3. Walking

_____

_____

4. Cross-training

_____

_____

5. Circuit training

_____

_____

Show What You Know

Tessa is a 54-year-old housewife who started exercising three months ago on the recommendation of her physician. Tessa has a BMI of 32, elevated triglycerides, and a total cholesterol value of 234 mg/dL. She has been walking for an accumulated 60 minutes per day and has worked her way up to walking continuously for up to 45 of those minutes. How could periodization help Tessa maximize her health-improvement goals?

_____

_____

_____

_____

_____

_____

_____

CHAPTER 11

The Metabolic Syndrome

Getting Started

This chapter defines the metabolic syndrome and covers its epidemiology and diagnostic criteria. The clinical implications and their associated disorders are also presented, along with the role of exercise in the prevention and treatment of the metabolic syndrome. Exercise programming and progression guidelines are also discussed. After completing this section, you will have a better understanding of:

- The various treatments of the metabolic syndrome, including dietary, pharmacological, and surgical treatments
- The body's physiological responses to exercise in the presence of the metabolic syndrome

Reading Assignment

Read Chapter 11 of the *ACE Advanced Health & Fitness Specialist Manual,* paying special attention to the boldface terms and the case study at the back of the chapter. After you have read the chapter, define the boldface terms on a separate piece of paper.

Expand Your Knowledge

I. Fill in the blanks.

a. Only about _____ of individuals with the metabolic syndrome have a body mass index (BMI) that is less than 25 kg/m^2.

b. It is typical for adiponectin levels to be _____ in obese individuals and those with the metabolic syndrome.

c. Values of high-sensitivity C-reactive protein greater than _____ may serve as a powerful predictor for future cardiovascular events.

d. Most individuals with a BMI equal to or greater than _____ have excess visceral adiposity, irrespective of body shape.

e. The main therapeutic target for treatment of the metabolic syndrome is _____.

f. Dietary intervention for the metabolic syndrome should include mainly consumption of _____ and _____ fatty acids, rather than _____ and trans fatty acids.

g. _____ surgery has a high success rate for treating obesity, as well as for improving all components of the metabolic syndrome.

h. Compared to individuals without the metabolic syndrome, those with the diagnostic criteria have about a _____ risk of developing type 2 diabetes and a _____ relative risk of developing cardiovascular disease.

II. List the five criteria used by the National Cholesterol Education Adult Treatment Panel III to define the metabolic syndrome.

1._____

_____

2._____

_____

3._____

_____

4._____

_____

5._____

_____

III. *Complete the following table by filling in the recommended intake of nutrients for the Therapeutic Lifestyle Changes (TLC) Diet.*

Nutrient	Recommended Intake
Saturated fat	
Polyunsaturated fat	
Monounsaturated fat	
Total fat	
Carbohydrate	
Fiber	
Protein	
Cholesterol	
Total calories	

IV. *Pharmacotherapies used to treat the metabolic syndrome typically target which four health conditions?*

1._____

2._____

3._____

4._____

V. Describe the pathophysiology that occurs when an individual transitions from the metabolic syndrome to overt type 2 diabetes.

_____

_____

_____

_____

_____

_____

VI. Explain the physiological reasons why physical inactivity predisposes a person to the metabolic syndrome.

_____

_____

_____

_____

_____

_____

VII. Describe the mechanisms by which the metabolic syndrome may contribute to respiratory stress during exertion.

_____

_____

_____

_____

_____

_____

VIII. Complete the physical-activity recommendations for clients with the metabolic syndrome.

1. Frequency:

_____

_____

_____

_____

2. Intensity:

_____

_____

_____

_____

3. Time:

_____

_____

_____

_____

4. Type:

_____

_____

_____

_____

Show What You Know

Jason, a 63-year-old retired attorney, recently had his annual physical. The results are listed below.

Height: 5'10" (1.8 m)
Weight: 200 lb (90 kg)
Waist circumference: 43" (109 cm)
Blood pressure: 140/82 mmHg
Fasting glucose: 148 mg/dL
Triglycerides: 222 mg/dL
HDL: 27 mg/dL

Based on this data, determine if Jason meets the criteria for the metabolic syndrome and discuss how a program of regular physical activity would influence each of the data presented.

_____

_____

_____

_____

_____

_____

_____

_____

CHAPTER 12

Diabetes Mellitus

Getting Started

This chapter begins by presenting the etiology of the various forms of diabetes mellitus, including type 1, type 2, and gestational diabetes. The role of exercise in diabetes management is also covered, as well as guidelines for exercise programming for individuals with each type of this disease. In addition, this chapter supplies information on how the ACE-AHFS can minimize the risks of exercise for these populations. After completing this section, you will have a better understanding of:

- The benefits of exercise for clients with diabetes mellitus
- The medical concerns associated with diabetes mellitus, including retinopathy, nephropathy, and neuropathy
- How to safely progress an exercise program for a client with diabetes
- Pre-exercise screening and client assessment, including acquiring physician approval before a program begins

Reading Assignment

Read Chapter 12 of the *ACE Advanced Health & Fitness Specialist Manual,* paying special attention to the bold-face terms and the case studies at the back of the chapter. After you have read the chapter, define the boldface terms on a separate piece of paper.

Expand Your Knowledge

I. Fill in the space to the left of each letter by placing (T1DM) if the statement describes type 1 diabetes and (T2DM) if it describes type 2 diabetes. Some statements may apply to both T1DM and T2DM.

_____a. An immune-mediated disease that selectively destroys the pancreatic beta cells

_____b. Accounts for 90–95% of all cases of diabetes mellitus

_____c. Most commonly diagnosed in persons younger than 30 years old

_____d. Linked with chronic abnormalities that worsen macrovascular, microvascular, and neural disease processes

_____e. Between 80 and 85% of those diagnosed with this disease are obese

_____f. Typically afflicts individuals older than 30 years of age

_____g. Lifestyle interventions focusing on weight loss and physical activity are the cornerstones of treatment for this disease

_____h. The absolute lack of insulin associated with this condition requires exogenous insulin administration

_____i. Neuropathy is experienced in about 65% of those diagnosed with this condition

_____j. Episodes of ketoacidosis are common for those diagnosed with this disease

II. List the American Diabetes Association's diagnostic criteria for diabetes mellitus.

_____

_____

_____

_____

III. *Explain the common complications associated with macrovascular and microvascular disease in individuals with diabetes.*

_____

_____

_____

_____

_____

_____

_____

_____

_____

IV. *Describe any exercise-related concerns associated with the use of insulin injections or infusion and oral hypoglycemic agents.*

_____

_____

_____

_____

_____

_____

_____

_____

_____

_____

_____

_____

_____

V. List the "ABC's" of diabetes and provide the established recommendations for each.

_____

_____

_____

VI. Explain the long-term physiological effects of regular exercise on individuals with type 1 diabetes and type 2 diabetes.

_____

_____

_____

_____

_____

_____

_____

_____

_____

_____

_____

_____

_____

_____

_____

VII. List the situations in which an exercise stress test is advisable for clients with diabetes.

_____

_____

_____

_____

VIII. Explain the differences in aerobic exercise programming for type 1 and type 2 diabetics.

_____

_____

_____

_____

_____

_____

_____

_____

IX. List four important practical tips for clients to remember when utilizing self–blood glucose monitoring (SBGM) with physical activity.

1._____

_____

2._____

_____

3._____

_____

4._____

_____

X. List six dysfunctional changes in a diabetic client that warrant referring the client back to his or her physician.

1._____

2._____

3._____

4._____

5._____

6._____

XI. Define the following conditions and explain how each is affected by an acute bout of exercise.

1. Hypoinsulinemia:

_____

_____

_____

_____

_____

2. Hyperinsulinemia

_____

_____

_____

_____

_____

XII. List seven characteristics that may be present in a client who is experiencing hypoglycemia or an insulin reaction.

1._____

2._____

3._____

4._____

5._____

6._____

XIII. Describe the appropriate timing and site of insulin injection for diabetic persons who are physically active.

_____

_____

_____

XIV. List the physical-activity precautions and limitations associated with each of the following conditions.

1. Retinopathy:

_____

_____

_____

_____

2. Nephropathy:

_____

_____

_____

_____

3. Neuropathy:

_____

_____

_____

_____

_____

_____

_____

Show What You Know

Marcia has type 1 diabetes and does an exceptional job of self–blood glucose monitoring (SBGM). She has just completed her third set of the leg press exercise. Upon questioning her regarding her perceived exertion for the set, she complains of lightheadedness and feeling shaky. What are the most appropriate actions for Marcia to take at this point in the exercise session?

_____

_____

_____

_____

_____

_____

_____

_____

CHAPTER 13

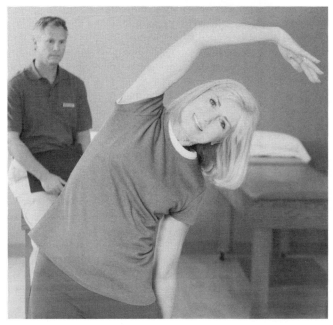

Posture and Movement

Getting Started

This chapter offers an overview of postural assessment, moving from the ankle up to the neck and head. Several movement screens are explained and demonstrated, after which examples of restorative exercises and exercises for mobility and stability are provided. After completing this section, you will have a better understanding of:

- Physiological properties associated with muscle imbalances, including the length-tension relationship and the force-couple relationship
- The right angle design of the body
- How to lead a client through several postural assessments and movement screens and use the results to identify postural issues
- How to distinguish between correctible postural problems and those that are not correctible through exercise

Reading Assignment

Read Chapter 13 of the *ACE Advanced Health & Fitness Specialist Manual,* paying special attention to the bold-face terms and the case study at the back of the chapter. After you have read the chapter, define the boldface terms on a separate piece of paper.

Expand Your Knowledge

I. Explain the relationship between the following words or phrases.

1. Activation threshold and hypertonic muscles

_____

_____

_____

2. Agonist and synergist

_____

_____

_____

3. Thoracic kyphosis and osteoporosis

_____

_____

_____

4. Side dominance and posture symmetry

_____

_____

_____

5. Dorsiflexion and overpronation

_____

_____

_____

6. Bowlegs and hip rotation

_____

_____

_____

7. Static stretching and muscle spindle activity

_____

_____

_____

_____

_____

II. *Fill in the space to the left of each letter by placing (KL) if the statement describes kyphosis-lordosis posture, (SW) if it describes swayback posture, (FB) if it describes flat-back posture, and (L) if it describes lordotic posture. Some statements may apply to more than one type of posture.*

_____a. Posterior pelvic tilt, forward translation of the pelvis, and a flattening of the lumbar curve

_____b. Anterior pelvic tilt, increased lordosis, and plantarflexion

_____c. Forward head and hyperextended knees

_____d. Hypertonic hamstrings and upper fibers of the internal obliques and lengthened one-joint hip flexors and upper-back extensors

_____e. Hypertonic neck extensors and rectus abdominis and lengthened lumbar extensors and neck flexors

_____f. Hypertonic anterior chest and hip flexor muscles and lengthened hip extensors and upper-back extensors

III. Fill in the blanks.

a. The law of _____ posits that as joints bear weight and move abnormally, the body strives to discover paths of lesser resistance.

b. The orientation of the contractile proteins within the sarcomere is the basis for the muscle-force generation principle called _____.

c. A sarcomere can generally stretch up to _____ of its resting length.

d. Following sustained periods of passive elongation of a tight muscle, series of additional _____ are added to help restore the muscle's normal tension-producing capabilities.

e. The legs and trunk provide _____ of the total kinetic energy and total force required to produce overhead activities, whereas the shoulder contributes _____ of the total energy and _____ of the total force.

f. When standing in neutral posture, the scapulae should lie flat against the upper back with up to _____ of forward rotation in the frontal plane.

g. Children under the age of _____ generally exhibit good posture, whereas individuals in their _____ may have entrenched poor postural habits.

h. When compensatory movements occur during active muscle contraction, it is usually indicative of _____.

IV. List the four main muscle groups involved in force-couple relationships that stabilize the pelvis in the sagittal plane and describe each muscle's action on the pelvis.

1._____

_____

2._____

_____

3._____

_____

4._____

_____

V. Describe how the ACE-AHFS can best determine a client's subtalar position during a static postural assessment.

_____

_____

_____

_____

_____

_____

_____

_____

VI. List the common deviations likely seen at each of the following anatomical structures during a static postural assessment.

1. Ankle and foot:

_____

_____

_____

2. Knee:

_____

_____

_____

3. Lumbo-pelvic region and hip:

_____

_____

_____

4. Thoracic spine and shoulders:

_____

_____

_____

5. Neck and head:

_____

_____

_____

VII. After each movement screen, write its primary assessment objective.

1. Forward bend and return:

_____

_____

2. Modified hurdle step stand:

_____

_____

3. Active straight-leg raise:

_____

_____

4. Active lordosis with active knee extension and ankle dorsiflexion:

_____

_____

5. Active lordosis with active hip flexion:

_____

_____

6. Standing wall screens:

_____

_____

VIII. Complete the table by filling in the modality associated with the key steps of restorative exercise programming.

Restorative Progress Steps	Modality
Inhibit hypertonic muscles	
Lengthen hypertonic muscles	
Activation of latent muscles	
Integration into functional movement	

IX. Explain the "stretch-then-strengthen" approach to restorative exercise programming.

_____

_____

_____

_____

_____

X. *Explain the importance of strengthening the muscles of the scapulothoracic region for ideal posture.*

_____

_____

_____

_____

_____

_____

_____

_____

Practice What You Know

I. *Practice performing on your current clients each of the posture assessments and movement screens described in Chapter 13. Use the posture assessment checklist and anterior/posterior and sagittal worksheets to familiarize yourself with the process of recording important client posture and movement information.*

II. *Using the restorative exercise programming guidelines (Table 13-20), develop programs to address the posture and movement deviations you discovered while practicing the assessments and screens on your clients.*

CHAPTER 14

Mobility, Gait, and Balance

Getting Started

This chapter begins with an examination of the core musculature and how it contributes to maintaining balance and facilitating movement. Several assessments of core function are discussed, including various muscle-endurance tests as well as a thorough gait analysis. Finally, a five-stage programming process is presented that will enable the ACE-AHFS to safely progress their clients' workouts. After completing this section, you will have a better understanding of:

- The myofascial slings
- How to interpret core function assessments and use that knowledge in your exercise programming
- The five-stage programming process: muscle activation and isolation, spinal stabilization, whole-body stabilization, core conditioning, and core power
- Exercises specifically designed to address gait and mobility

Reading Assignment

Read Chapter 14 of the *ACE Advanced Health & Fitness Specialist Manual,* paying special attention to the boldface terms and the case study at the back of the chapter. After you have read the chapter, define the boldface terms on a separate piece of paper.

Expand Your Knowledge

I. List five factors that may reduce a person's limits of stability (LOS).

1. _____

2. _____

3. _____

4. _____

5. _____

II. Define the three measurable dimensions of balance.

1. Anticipatory control:

_____

_____

_____

2. Reactive control:

_____

_____

_____

3. Adaptive postural control:

_____

_____

_____

III. List and describe the three postural strategies that are used to respond to disturbances in balance.

_____

_____

_____

_____

_____

_____

_____

_____

IV. List the muscles associated with each layer of the core anatomy and describe each layer's contribution to stability and/or movement of the trunk.

   1. Deep layer:

_____

_____

_____

   2. Middle layer:

_____

_____

_____

_____

_____

_____

3. Outer layer:

_____

_____

_____

V. *Explain the importance of the role of the transverse abdominis in spinal stabilization and describe its association with low-back pain.*

_____

_____

_____

_____

_____

_____

_____

_____

VI. *Explain the difference between abdominal hollowing and abdominal bracing and indicate which one is most effective for spinal stabilization during physical activity.*

_____

_____

_____

_____

_____

_____

_____

_____

VII. Describe four characteristics necessary for a person to achieve a normal gait pattern.

1. _____

2. _____

3. _____

4. _____

VIII. List and describe the functions of the key muscles groups involved during each instant of gait.

1. Initial contact and load response:

_____

_____

_____

2. Midstance:

_____

_____

_____

3. Terminal stance:

_____

_____

_____

4. Pre-swing and initial swing:

_____

_____

_____

5. Initial swing and midswing:

_____

_____

_____

6. Midswing and terminal swing:

_____

_____

_____

IX. Explain the general concept of force closure as it relates to myofascial slings.

_____

_____

_____

_____

_____

_____

X. List the five primary human movements.

1. _____

     _____

2. _____

     _____

3. _____

     _____

4. _____

     _____

5. _____

     _____

XI. Explain the difference in Q-angle between males and females and describe the relationship between Q-angle and knee stability.

_____

_____

_____

_____

_____

XII. Fill in the space to the left of each letter by placing (AADL) if the statement describes advanced activities of daily living, (IADL) if it describes instrumental activities of daily living, and (BADL) if it describes basic activities of daily living.

_____a. Dusting and sweeping to prepare for visitors

_____b. Weekly grocery shopping

_____c. Drawing and taking a nightly bath

_____d. Tending to a rose garden

_____e. Doing laundry and carrying it in a laundry basket

_____f. Dressing for breakfast

_____g. Going on an all-senior cruise trip

XIII. List the five functional prerequisite goals for developing a solid foundation for effective exercise programming.

1._____

2._____

3._____

4._____

5._____

XIV. List the primary programming objectives for each core-conditioning stage.

1. Muscle activation and isolation:

_____

_____

2. Core stabilization:

_____

_____

3. Whole-body stabilization:

_____

_____

4. Core conditioning:

_____

_____

5. Core power:

_____

_____

XV. List the four specific requirements necessary for coordinated movement.

1._____

_____

2._____

_____

3._____

_____

4._____

_____

Practice What You Know

I. *Practice performing on your current clients each of the core function and gait analysis assessments described in Chapter 14. Create your own assessment worksheets to familiarize yourself with the process of recording important client core function and gait information.*

II. *Using the template for progressing core-conditioning stages (Table 14-3), develop programs to address the core function and gait deviations you discovered while practicing the assessments on your clients.*

CHAPTER 15

Arthritis

Getting Started

This chapter explains the epidemiology of arthritis and differentiates between osteoarthritis and rheumatoid arthritis. A thorough examination of physical symptoms and findings associated with this disease is included, along with programming guidelines and considerations for working with clients with arthritis. After completing this section, you will have a better understanding of:

- The normal course of symptoms in an osteoarthritic joint
- The etiology of medical conditions and how to differentiate between primary and secondary conditions
- Which exercises are safe to include in a program for a client with, or at risk for, arthritis, as well as movements that are unsafe and therefore contraindicated

Reading Assignment

Read Chapter 15 of the *ACE Advanced Health & Fitness Specialist Manual,* paying special attention to the boldface terms and the case study at the back of the chapter. After you have read the chapter, define the boldface terms on a separate piece of paper.

Expand Your Knowledge

I. Describe the major differences between the following pairs of words or phrases.

1. Rheumatoid arthritis and osteoarthritis

_____

_____

_____

2. Primary etiology and secondary etiology

_____

_____

_____

3. Acute injury and insidious onset

_____

_____

_____

4. Type A synovial cells and type B synovial cells

_____

_____

_____

5. Joint capsule and synovial membrane

_____

_____

_____

6. Grade 1 articular damage and grade 4 articular damage

_____

_____

_____

II. *Describe the three phases of rheumatoid arthritis progression.*

1._____

_____

2._____

_____

3._____

_____

III. *List the three primary factors that specify the structural integrity of a joint.*

1._____

_____

2._____

_____

3._____

_____

IV. *Describe the three protective functions provided to a joint by healthy articular cartilage.*

1._____

_____

2._____

_____

3._____

_____

V. *Explain the process of deterioration related to osteoarthritis from the initial disruption of articular cartilage to the exposure of subchondral bone.*

_____

_____

_____

_____

_____

_____

_____

VI. *List 10 criteria for the diagnosis of osteoarthritis of the knee.*

1._____

2._____

3._____

4._____

5._____

6._____

7._____

8._____

9._____

10._____

VII. *List five categories of individuals who are at an increased risk for osteoarthritis.*

1._____

2._____

3._____

4._____

5._____

VIII. Discuss the benefits of regular exercise for individuals with osteoarthritis.

_____

_____

_____

_____

_____

_____

_____

_____

IX. Fill in the blanks.

a. Of those who have osteoarthritis, _____ will have movement limitations and _____ cannot perform major activities of daily living.

b. The most common anatomical sites affected by osteoarthritis are the _____, _____, _____, _____, and _____.

c. The vast majority of osteoarthritis cases are secondary in nature, with the primary causes being _____ and/or _____.

d. Articular cartilage has no _____ and thus cannot heal if injured, and is void of _____.

e. Initial symptoms of osteoarthritis are next-day discomfort and/or _____.

f. Temporary relief from osteoarthritis symptoms can be achieved with over-the-counter _____ and/or _____.

Show What You Know

Beth is a 54-year-old nurse who was diagnosed with osteoarthritis in both knees several years ago. She claims that pain interferes with recreational activities and work, and admits that weight management is difficult, especially since she is uncomfortable doing most weightbearing activities. The most notable data obtained during Beth's initial health and fitness evaluation was a BMI of 29 kg/m², blood pressure of 142/95 mmHg, and a considerable lack of range of motion in her lower extremities. How should the ACE-AHFS proceed with exercise programming for this client?

CHAPTER 16

Osteoporosis and Osteopenia

Getting Started

This chapter offers an explanation of the factors that affect bone, including age, genetics, lifestyle factors, and nutrition, and discusses special considerations associated with bone health, including menopause and the female athlete triad. This chapter also includes a summary of bone's response to loading, hormonal intervention, and nutritional intervention. Programming and progression guidelines are also presented. After completing this section, you will have a better understanding of:

- The organization of bone
- The treatment of osteoporosis and osteopenia, including non-pharmacological treatments, pharmacological treatments, surgical interventions, and exercise
- The physiological bone responses to exercise in various age groups, including children and adolescents, pre- and postmenopausal women, and men
- How programming and progression guidelines vary among those same age groups

Reading Assignment

Read Chapter 16 of the *ACE Advanced Health & Fitness Specialist Manual,* paying special attention to the bold-face terms and the case studies at the back of the chapter. After you have read the chapter, define the boldface terms on a separate piece of paper.

Expand Your Knowledge

I. Match each term with its associated descriptive statement.

_____a. Considered the most devastating type of osteoporosis-related fracture

_____b. A condition of reduced skeletal mass that warrants close monitoring to ensure that it does not worsen over time

_____c. Less than 10% of these osteoporosis-related fractures result in hospital admission

_____d. Forms a dense shell around the skeleton and constitutes the thick shafts of long bones

_____e. Forms a lattice-like network, which greatly increases surface area for metabolic activity within the skeleton

_____f. The cycle of bone remodeling that consists of bone removal

_____g. Improves bone strength by adding mass and expanding the inner and outer diameters of bone

_____h. Cells responsible for bone resorption

_____i. Cells responsible for bone formation

_____j. The physiological process of replacing damaged bone tissue with an equal amount of new bone tissue

1. Trabecular bone

2. Vertebral fracture

3. Osteopenia

4. Resorption

5. Hip fracture

6. Cortical bone

7. Modeling

8. Remodeling

9. Osteoblasts

10. Osteoclasts

II. Briefly explain how each of the following factors affects an individual's bone mineral density (BMD).

1. Age:

_____

_____

_____

_____

2. Sex:

_____

_____

_____

_____

_____

3. Genetics:

_____

_____

_____

_____

_____

4. Race:

_____

_____

_____

_____

_____

5. Estrogen:

_____

_____

_____

_____

_____

6. Smoking:

_____

_____

_____

_____

_____

7. Alcohol consumption:

_____

_____

_____

_____

_____

8. Caffeine consumption:

_____

_____

_____

_____

_____

9. Calcium and vitamin D intake:

_____

_____

_____

_____

_____

III. Define the female athlete triad and describe how it affects BMD in women.

_____

_____

_____

_____

_____

_____

IV. List seven common symptoms experienced by women who are in the perimenopausal stage.

1._____

2._____

3._____

4._____

5._____

6._____

7._____

V. According the National Osteoporosis Foundation, what three population groups should undergo BMD testing?

1._____

2._____

3._____

4._____

VI. Fill in the space to the left of each letter by placing (DEXA) if the statement describes dual-energy x-ray absorptiometry, (QUS) if it describes quantitative ultrasound, or (QCT) if it describes quantitative computed tomography.

_____a. Uses two transducers that are positioned on each side of the tissue to be measured

_____b. Provides a three-dimensional measure of trabecular and cortical bone

_____c. Measures an areal density of bone and body composition

_____d. Advantages include low radiation exposure, high accuracy, and the ability to measure small changes in BMD over time

_____e. Disadvantages include poor precision and accuracy and relatively high doses of radiation

_____f. One possible advantage is the measurement of characteristics of bone strength that are potentially independent of BMD

_____g. Based on the principle that bone attenuates the most energy, followed by muscle, and then fat

VII. Describe how the following drugs act in the body to improve an individual's BMD.

1. Calcitonin:

_____

_____

_____

_____

2. Bisphosphonates:

_____

_____

_____

_____

3. Selective estrogen receptor modulators (SERMs):

_____

_____

_____

_____

4. Parathyroid hormone:

_____

_____

_____

_____

5. Strontium ranelate:

_____

_____

_____

_____

VIII. List six basic principles regarding the best type of exercise (loading) to produce optimal enhancements in BMD.

1._____

_____

_____

2._____

_____

_____

3._____

_____

_____

4._____

_____

_____

5._____

_____

_____

6._____

_____

_____

IX. Complete the FITT principle for children and young adults for enhancing bone health.

1. Frequency:

_____

_____

2. Intensity:

_____

_____

3. Time:

_____

_____

4. Type:

_____

_____

X. Explain the benefits of performing strength-training exercises in a standing, weightbearing position.

_____

_____

_____

_____

_____

_____

XI. Explain the recommendations and precautions for exercise for clients who have been diagnosed with osteoporosis.

_____

_____

_____

_____

_____

_____

_____

Show What You Know

Olivia is a 60-year-old postmenopausal Caucasian woman who is seeking the services of an ACE-AHFS for help with improving her BMD through exercise training. She went through menopause at age 48 and has been in good general health for the past several years. Olivia has no personal history of fractures, but her older sister experienced a hip fracture. She is 5'7" (1.7 m) and weighs 112 pounds (50 kg), smokes cigarettes, drinks several cups of coffee a day, and rarely exercises. A recent BMD test revealed a left hip T-score of −1.5, placing her in the osteopenia category. Apart from a regular exercise program, what other recommendations can you give Olivia to help modify her lifestyle to improve bone health?

CHAPTER 17

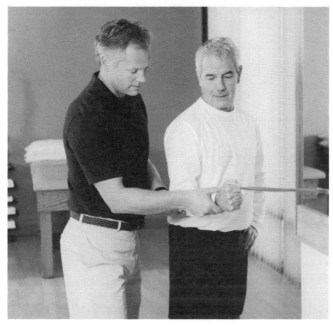

Principles of Post-orthopedic Rehabilitation

Getting Started

This chapter walks the ACE-AHFS through the initial interview and objective evaluation of a new post-orthopedic rehabilitation client, maintaining a consistent focus on the importance of clear and concise communication with the client's healthcare team. Concepts of healing are also discussed, along with a systematic progression of programming. After completing this section, you will have a better understanding of:

- How to create an accurate and concise assessment summary
- How to use rehabilitation protocols when working with these clients without straying outside the ACE-AHFS scope of practice
- The systematic progression of programming, which includes four steps: increasing range of motion and flexibility, improving aerobic condition, returning to physical activity, and building strength and power

Reading Assignment

Read Chapter 17 of the *ACE Advanced Health & Fitness Specialist Manual,* paying special attention to the boldface terms and the case studies at the back of the chapter. After you have read the chapter, define the boldface terms on a separate piece of paper.

Expand Your Knowledge

I. *Explain why it is crucial to glean information from a client's medical team after he or she has been released from orthopedic rehabilitation and is ready to begin a community-based exercise program.*

_____

_____

_____

_____

_____

_____

_____

_____

II. *Describe the importance of questioning a client regarding his or her level of pain or discomfort during the initial interview and throughout the progression of the exercise program.*

_____

_____

_____

_____

_____

_____

_____

_____

III. *Discuss the reasons why the ACE-AHFS should maintain a working knowledge of established rehabilitation protocols for common orthopedic injuries and conditions.*

_____

_____

_____

_____

_____

_____

IV. *Complete the table by filling in the description, objective, and duration of each phase of tissue healing.*

Phase	Description	Objective	Duration
Inflammation			
Proliferation			
Remodeling			

V. *Explain the differences in approach to stretching healthy tissue versus stretching tissue that has been injured.*

_____

_____

_____

_____

_____

_____

_____

VI. Describe how improving a post-orthopedic rehabilitation client's aerobic condition can enhance his or her overall physiological and psychological health.

_____

_____

_____

_____

_____

_____

_____

VII. List four objectives that will provide a post-orthopedic rehabilitation client with a good foundation for transitioning to a physically active lifestyle.

1._____

2._____

3._____

4._____

CHAPTER 18

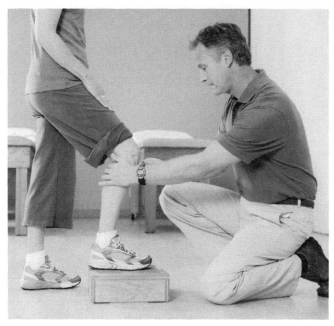

Musculoskeletal Injuries of the Lower Extremity

Getting Started

This chapter explains the principles of restorative exercise, including flexibility, strengthening, and functional integration. Each of these three topics is included in the discussion of the various hip, knee, ankle, and foot injuries covered in this chapter. Muscle strains and structural abnormalities are also discussed. After completing this section, you will have a better understanding of:

- The following hip pathologies: trochanteric bursitis, iliotibial band friction syndrome, hip osteoarthritis, and total hip replacements
- The following knee pathologies: patellofemoral pain syndrome, meniscal injuries, ACL injuries, and total knee replacements
- The following ankle and foot pathologies: ankle sprains, plantar fasciitis, Achilles tendinopathy, and shin splints

Reading Assignment

Read Chapter 18 of the *ACE Advanced Health & Fitness Specialist Manual,* paying special attention to the bold-face terms and the case studies at the back of the chapter. After you have read the chapter, define the boldface terms on a separate piece of paper.

Expand Your Knowledge

I. *List six questions that the ACE-AHFS can ask a client to aid in determining if it is appropriate for the client to begin a restorative exercise program.*

1. _____

2. _____

3. _____

4. _____

5. _____

6. _____

II. *Explain the difference between open kinetic chain (OKC) and closed kinetic chain (CKC) exercise and indicate which one is most beneficial from a functional integration perspective.*

_____

_____

_____

_____

_____

III. *Describe the general concept of proprioception as it relates to restorative exercise and the functional integration of a client back into his or her normal activities of daily living.*

_____

_____

_____

_____

_____

_____

IV. For each of the following lower-extremity pathologies, list the etiology, signs and symptoms, and precautions for physical activity.

　1. Trochanteric bursitis
　　a. Etiology:

　　_____

　　_____

　　_____

　　_____

　　b. Signs and symptoms:

　　_____

　　_____

　　_____

　　_____

　　c. Precautions:

　　_____

　　_____

　　_____

　　_____

　2. Iliotibial band friction syndrome (ITBFS)
　　a. Etiology:

　　_____

　　_____

　　_____

　　_____

b. Signs and symptoms:

_____

_____

_____

_____

c. Precautions:

_____

_____

_____

_____

3. Hip osteoarthritis (OA)
   a. Etiology:

_____

_____

_____

b. Signs and symptoms:

_____

_____

_____

_____

c. Precautions:

_____

_____

_____

_____

4. Total hip replacement
   a. Etiology:

_____

_____

_____

_____

   b. Signs and symptoms:

_____

_____

_____

_____

   c. Precautions:

_____

_____

_____

_____

5. Patellofemoral pain syndrome (PFPS)
   a. Etiology:

_____

_____

_____

_____

   b. Signs and symptoms:

_____

_____

_____

_____

   c. Precautions:

_____

_____

_____

_____

6. Meniscal injuries
   a. Etiology:

_____

_____

_____

_____

b. Signs and symptoms:

_____

_____

_____

_____

c. Precautions:

_____

_____

_____

_____

7. Anterior cruciate ligament (ACL) injuries
   a. Etiology:

_____

_____

_____

_____

   b. Signs and symptoms:

_____

_____

_____

_____

c. Precautions:

_____

_____

_____

_____

8. Total knee replacement (TKR)
   a. Etiology:

_____

_____

_____

_____

   b. Signs and symptoms:

_____

_____

_____

_____

   c. Precautions:

_____

_____

_____

_____

9. Ankle sprains
   a. Etiology:

_____

_____

_____

_____

   b. Signs and symptoms:

_____

_____

_____

_____

   c. Precautions:

_____

_____

_____

_____

10. Plantar fasciitis
   a. Etiology:

_____

_____

_____

_____

b. Signs and symptoms:

_____

_____

_____

_____

c. Precautions:

_____

_____

_____

_____

11. Achilles tendinopathy
   a. Etiology:

_____

_____

_____

_____

   b. Signs and symptoms:

_____

_____

_____

_____

    c. Precautions:

_____

_____

_____

_____

12. Shin splints
    a. Etiology:

_____

_____

_____

_____

    b. Signs and symptoms:

_____

_____

_____

_____

    c. Precautions:

_____

_____

_____

_____

V. Describe the three common total hip replacement procedures performed by surgeons.

1. Primary:

_____

_____

_____

2. Hemiarthroplasty:

_____

_____

_____

3. Hip resurfacing:

_____

_____

_____

VI. List 11 early-intervention strategies to alleviate patella femoral pain syndrome.

1._____

2._____

3._____

4._____

5._____

6._____

7._____

8._____

9._____

10._____

11._____

VII. List the five important functions the meniscal cartilage performs at the knee joint.

1. _____

2. _____

3. _____

4. _____

5. _____

VIII. Briefly describe the following surgical procedures used to repair ACL injuries.

1. Patellar tendon graft:

_____

_____

_____

_____

2. Hamstring tendon graft:

_____

_____

_____

_____

3. Allograft:

_____

_____

_____

_____

IX. Describe the early-intervention strategy of PRICE for treating ankle sprains.

_____

_____

_____

_____

_____

_____

Practice What You Know

Review the lower-extremity pathologies listed in Chapter 18 and determine which conditions you have encountered or are likely to encounter frequently with your client base. Develop general restorative exercise programs for the pathologies you have selected based on the information presented in the chapter as well as established protocols for the conditions.

CHAPTER 19

Musculoskeletal Injuries of the Upper Extremity

Getting Started

This chapter picks up where the previous chapter leaves off by discussing the importance of being aware of the mechanism of injury, the structures involved, the healing constraints of the structures involved, exacerbating activities, and range-of-motion issues. After completing this section, you will have a better understanding of:

- The importance of communicating with a client's physical therapist and physician, especially regarding recurrent pain, instability, and loss of range of motion
- The following injuries: acromioclavicular joint injuries, shoulder instability, rotator cuff pathology, lateral epicondylitis, medial epicondylitis, and hand and wrist injuries

Reading Assignment

Read Chapter 19 of the *ACE Advanced Health & Fitness Specialist Manual,* paying special attention to the boldface terms and the case studies at the back of the chapter. After you have read the chapter, define the boldface terms on a separate piece of paper.

Expand Your Knowledge

I. For each of the following upper-extremity pathologies, list the etiology, signs and symptoms, and precautions for physical activity.

1. Acromioclavicular joint injuries
   a. Etiology:

   _____

   _____

   _____

   b. Signs and symptoms:

   _____

   _____

   _____

   c. Precautions:

   _____

   _____

   _____

2. Shoulder instability
   a. Etiology:

   _____

   _____

   _____

   b. Signs and symptoms:

   _____

   _____

   _____

c. Precautions:

_____

_____

_____

3. Rotator cuff injuries
   a. Etiology:

   _____

   _____

   _____

   b. Signs and symptoms:

   _____

   _____

   _____

   c. Precautions:

   _____

   _____

   _____

4. Lateral epicondylitis
   a. Etiology:

   _____

   _____

   _____

b. Signs and symptoms:

_____

_____

_____

c. Precautions:

_____

_____

_____

5. Medial epicondylitis
   a. Etiology:

_____

_____

_____

   b. Signs and symptoms:

_____

_____

_____

   c. Precautions:

_____

_____

_____

6. Carpal tunnel syndrome
    a. Etiology:

_____

_____

_____

    b. Signs and symptoms:

_____

_____

_____

    c. Precautions:

_____

_____

_____

7. De Quervain's syndrome
    a. Etiology:

_____

_____

_____

    b. Signs and symptoms:

_____

_____

_____

c. Precautions:

_____

_____

_____

II. *Explain the appropriate modifications for clients with anterior shoulder instability for the following exercises.*

1. Lat pull-down:

_____

_____

_____

2. Biceps curl:

_____

_____

_____

3. Bench press:

_____

_____

_____

4. Shoulder press:

_____

_____

_____

_____

III. Explain why movements in the scapular plane are best for strengthening the shoulder in clients with impingement syndrome.

_____

_____

_____

_____

_____

_____

IV. Discuss the reasons why multijoint exercises for the upper body are appropriate for clients who have experienced lateral epicondylitis.

_____

_____

_____

_____

_____

Practice What You Know

Review the upper-extremity pathologies listed in Chapter 19 and determine which conditions you have encountered or are likely to encounter frequently with your client base. Develop general restorative exercise programs for the pathologies you have selected based on the information presented in the chapter as well as established protocols for the conditions.

CHAPTER 20

Low-back Pain

Getting Started

This chapter covers the many factors that can contribute to low-back pain and offers an overview of conditions. The role of exercise in managing low-back pain is discussed in detail, as are exercise programming guidelines and considerations. Several key exercises and explained and demonstrated. After completing this section, you will have a better understanding of:

- The various treatments for low-back pain, including non-pharmacologic therapy, pharmacologic therapy, injections, and surgery
- Caveats for designing exercise programs for back health
- The five stages for building the ultimate back, which begin with grooving motion patterns and continue through to the development of power

Reading Assignment

Read Chapter 20 of the *ACE Advanced Health & Fitness Specialist Manual,* paying special attention to the bold-face terms and the case study at the back of the chapter. After you have read the chapter, define the boldface terms on a separate piece of paper.

Expand Your Knowledge

I. Describe how the following factors may contribute to low-back pain (LBP).

1. Age:

_____

_____

_____

2. Sex:

_____

_____

_____

3. Body type:

_____

_____

_____

4. Smoking:

_____

_____

_____

5. Occupation:

_____

_____

_____

6. Exercise:

_____

_____

_____

7. Depression:

_____

_____

_____

II. Fill in the blanks.

a. More than _____ of Americans suffer from at least one episode of LBP during their lifetime.

b. Of the possible etiologies for LBP, _____ are mechanical causes, _____ are visceral disease, and _____ are spinal conditions such as tumors, infections, and rheumatologic disorders.

c. _____ refers to dysfunction or degeneration of lumbar intervertebral discs.

d. A _____ occurs when there is a tear in the annulus with a subsequent extrusion of the nucleus through this annular defect.

e. Nerve-root impairment, or _____, is associated with pain, numbness, tingling, or weakness.

f. A narrowing of the central spinal canal due to degenerative changes of the facet joints and intervertebral discs is called _____.

g. Spondylolysis is a stress fracture of the _____, whereas spondylolisthesis is

_____.

III. Describe how targeting each of the following sites for spinal injection with local anesthetics and/or corticosteroids may decrease pain for individuals with LBP.

1. Trigger point:

_____

_____

2. Facet:

_____

_____

3. Epidural:

_____

_____

IV. List the theoretical goals of each of the following categories of therapeutic exercise for LBP.

1. Flexion:

_____

_____

2. Extension:

_____

_____

3. Stabilization:

_____

_____

V. Explain Wendell's three stages of exercise progression for the treatment of LBP.

1. Centralization:

_____

_____

_____

_____

_____

2. Lumbar stabilization:

_____

_____

_____

_____

_____

3. Dynamic stabilization:

_____

_____

_____

_____

_____

VI. List eight contraindications/modifications the ACE-AHFS should be aware of when working with clients with a history of LBP.

1._____

_____

_____

2._____

_____

_____

3._____

_____

_____

4._____

_____

_____

5._____

_____

_____

6._____

_____

_____

7._____

_____

_____

8._____

_____

_____

VII. Explain McGill's argument that strength has little association with low-back health.

_____

_____

_____

_____

_____

_____

_____

VIII. Discuss how diurnal variations affect spinal stability.

_____

_____

_____

_____

_____

_____

_____

IX. List McGill's five stages for building the ultimate back.

1. _____

2. _____

3. _____

4. _____

5. _____

X. Compare the appropriateness of the traditional squat and the single-leg squat in an exercise program for
    enhancing back health for a client with "crossed-pelvis syndrome."

    _____

    _____

    _____

    _____

    _____

    _____

    _____

    _____

    _____

    _____

    _____

XI. List five basic considerations for developing back strength in a client who has progressed through grooving
    motion/motor patterns, building whole-body and joint stabilization, and increasing muscle endurance.

    1._____

    2._____

    3._____

    4._____

    5._____

Practice What You Know

I.   Practice performing on your current clients each of the tests for lumbar torsional control as indicated in
     Chapter 20 (Figures 20-1 through 20-3). Create your own assessment worksheets to familiarize yourself
     with the process of recording important client spine-stability data.

II. Using McGill's five stages for building the ultimate back, develop programs to address the lumbar devia-
     tions you discovered while practicing the assessments and screens on your clients.

CHAPTER 21

Older Adults

Getting Started

This chapter begins with an extensive discussion of the physical changes associated with aging, including changes in the body's systems as well changes in neuromuscular coordination and body composition. Balance and gait challenges for older adults are also covered. Progression and programming guidelines are presented, along with strategies for teaching exercise to older adults. After completing this section, you will have a better understanding of:

- The importance of functional training for activities of daily living
- How to assess older adult clients, including medications taken and overall physical function
- Nutritional considerations for older adults, especially as they related to sensory losses and structural changes

Reading Assignment

Read Chapter 21 of the *ACE Advanced Health & Fitness Specialist Manual,* paying special attention to the boldface terms and the case study at the back of the chapter. After you have read the chapter, define the boldface terms on a separate piece of paper.

Expand Your Knowledge

I.   Describe the major differences between the following pairs of words or phrases.

1. Lifespan and life expectancy

_____

_____

_____

2. Chronological age and functional age

_____

_____

_____

3. Residual volume and expiratory reserve volume

_____

_____

_____

4. Muscle atrophy and sarcopenia

_____

_____

_____

5. Neuromuscular coordination and hand-eye coordination

_____

_____

_____

II. *What is a possible explanation for the decline in maximum heart rate seen in older individuals?*

_____

_____

_____

_____

_____

_____

III. *List three possible reasons for the overall age-related decline in aerobic capacity in older adults.*

1._____

2._____

3._____

IV. *Discuss the factors that contribute to an overall loss of flexibility associated with aging.*

_____

_____

_____

_____

_____

_____

_____

V. Describe how memory is affected by the aging process and list techniques the ACE-AHFS can use to
    enhance the process of learning a new task for older adults.

_____

_____

_____

_____

_____

_____

VI. Explain the compensatory strategies often developed by older adults to cope with reduced neuromuscular
    efficiency and speed of performance.

1. Anticipation:

_____

_____

_____

_____

_____

2. Simplification:

_____

_____

_____

_____

3. Trading speed for accuracy:

_____

_____

_____

_____

_____

_____

VII. Explain how postural sway is related to an older adult's risk for falling.

_____

_____

_____

_____

_____

VIII. Describe how aging affects each of the three peripheral systems responsible for balance.

1. Visual system:

_____

_____

_____

_____

_____

_____

_____

2. Somatosensory system:

_____

_____

_____

_____

_____

_____

_____

3. Vestibular system:

_____

_____

_____

_____

_____

_____

IX. Discuss two possible explanations for the decreased gait speeds observed in older adults.

1. _____

_____

_____

_____

_____

_____

2. _____

_____

_____

_____

_____

_____

X. List the five age-related physiological changes that slow or diminish the pharmacokinetics of medications in older adults.

1. _____

2. _____

3. _____

4. _____

5. _____

XI. Write the assessment objectives and the most appropriate candidates for the following balance tests.

1. Berg Balance Scale (BBS):

_____

_____

_____

_____

_____

2. Fullerton Advanced Balance Scale (FAB):

_____

_____

_____

_____

_____

XII. Briefly describe the benefits of aquatic exercise in relation to balance training.

_____

_____

_____

_____

_____

_____

_____

_____

_____

XIII. List seven precautions to consider when using elastic resistance in an older adult's strength-training program.

1._____

2._____

3._____

4._____

5._____

6._____

7._____

XIV. Describe how the aging process affects an older adult's ability to obtain the following vitamins and minerals and list strategies for enhancing the intake of each nutrient in an older individual's diet.

1. Vitamin B12:

_____

_____

_____

_____

2. Vitamin C:

_____

_____

_____

_____

3. Vitamin D:

_____

_____

_____

_____

4. Calcium:

_____

_____

_____

_____

5. Iron:

_____

_____

_____

_____

6. Zinc:

_____

_____

_____

_____

XV. List five characteristics of Tufts University's Modified MyPyramid for Older Adults that distinguish it from the USDA's original MyPyramid.

1._____

_____

2._____

_____

3._____

_____

4._____

_____

5._____

_____

Practice What You Know

Visit www.easyforyou.info, complete the registration process, and print out the recommendations summary page. Use your experience navigating the website to educate your clients about the interactive features that may be useful for them and/or their peers.

CHAPTER 22

Youth

Getting Started

This chapter begins with an overview of the current health and fitness status of youth and a discussion of the many benefits of youth exercise. Youth fitness guidelines are presented along with an explanation of why it is so important to develop fundamental movement skills in children. Program design considerations are also discussed, including tips for how to develop fun, non-competitive games. After completing this section, you will have a better understanding of:

- How exercise affects growth and development in children
- How to provide effective leadership and instruction to youth, including adding variety, providing specific feedback, and enlisting parent support
- Nutrition and hydration guidelines for youth and how to incorporate these issues into your program without overstepping the ACE-AHFS scope of practice

Reading Assignment

Read Chapter 22 of the *ACE Advanced Health & Fitness Specialist Manual,* paying special attention to the boldface terms and the case study at the back of the chapter. After you have read the chapter, define the boldface terms on a separated piece of paper.

Expand Your Knowledge

I. *Fill in the blanks.*

    a. Over the past several years, the number of health club members between the ages of
        _____ increased by 58%.

    b. According to the Centers for Disease Control and Prevention, _____ of chil-
        dren ages nine to 13 do not participate in any organized physical activity during non-school hours,
        and only _____ of high school students attend physical education classes.

    c. Over the past three decades, the prevalence of obesity has _____ for adolescents
        and it has more than _____ for children.

    d. Type 2 diabetes now accounts for _____ of all new cases of diabetes in children
        and adolescents.

    e. Health-related behaviors that are acquired during childhood and adolescence are likely to be
        _____.

    f. Differences in height and weight among adolescents are related to the timing of
        _____, which typically occurs between the ages of _____ in
        girls and _____ in boys.

    g. With regard to respiration, children and adolescents have a higher breathing frequency and a lower
        _____ than adults at all exercise intensities.

    h. Children and adolescents also exhibit higher heart rates and lower _____ at all
        exercise intensities.

II. *List nine potential health and fitness benefits of youth strength training.*

    1._____

    2._____

    3._____

    4._____

    5._____

    6._____

    7._____

8. _____

9. _____

III. Explain the concept that children tend to be "metabolic non-specialists" with regards to fitness performance.

_____

_____

_____

_____

_____

IV. Discuss why it is important to avoid using "pass-fail" terminology when conducting fitness assessments for youth.

_____

_____

_____

_____

_____

V. Describe why it may be a good practice for the ACE-AHFS to focus on the accumulation of physical activity throughout the day for youth rather than continuous bouts of physical activity.

_____

_____

_____

_____

_____

VI. List six basic aerobic-training guidelines for youth.

1._____

2._____

3._____

4._____

5._____

6._____

VII. List eight basic strength-training guidelines for youth.

1._____

2._____

3._____

4._____

5._____

6._____

7._____

8._____

VIII. Describe a typical dynamic warm-up that would be appropriate to use with youth.

_____

_____

_____

_____

_____

_____

IX. Discuss the current view of the traditional anatomical concern associated with youth fitness and injury to the growth plate in young people.

_____

_____

_____

_____

_____

_____

_____

_____

X. List three leadership techniques that have proven effective for teaching physical activity to youth.

1._____

_____

2._____

_____

3._____

_____

XI. List five strategies to help foster healthy eating in young people.

1._____

_____

2._____

_____

3._____

_____

4._____

_____

5._____

_____

XII. Explain the importance of adequate hydration in youth.

_____

_____

_____

_____

_____

_____

_____

_____

_____

Practice What You Know

Visit a youth physical-activity program in your area and observe the environment in which it is held. Perform the summary checklist for creating games and activities for kids (Figure 22-1) to determine if the program meets the recommendations for a safe and effective exercise experience for youth.

CHAPTER 23

Pre- and Postnatal Exercise

Getting Started

This chapter begins with a discussion of the benefits and risks of exercise during pregnancy, including the fetal response to maternal exercise and contraindications and risk factors. Programming and progression guidelines for both pre- and postnatal exercise are presented, as well as biomechanical considerations for the lactating mother. After completing this section, you will have a better understanding of:

- The physiological changes associated with pregnancy, as well as biomechanical considerations, including diastasis recti and stress urinary incontinence
- Nutritional and psychological considerations when working with pregnant exercisers
- The physiological changes that take place following pregnancy

Reading Assignment

Read Chapter 23 of the *ACE Advanced Health & Fitness Specialist Manual*, paying special attention to the boldface terms and the case study at the back of the chapter. After you have read the chapter, define the boldface terms on a separate piece of paper.

Expand Your Knowledge

I.   Explain how physical activity during pregnancy can affect the following conditions.

1. Gestational diabetes (GDM):

_____

_____

_____

_____

2. Preeclampsia:

_____

_____

_____

_____

3. Maternal obesity:

_____

_____

_____

_____

II. Address the following theoretical concerns about the fetal response to maternal exercise.

1. Selective redistribution of blood flow away from the fetus:

_____

_____

_____

_____

2. Fetal tachycardia and increased blood pressure:

_____

_____

_____

_____

3. Intrauterine growth restriction:

_____

_____

_____

_____

III. Briefly describe the pregnancy-induced changes in the cardiovascular system (i.e., cardiac output, stroke volume, blood pressure, and heart rate).

_____

_____

_____

_____

IV. Explain the "training effect" of pregnancy.

_____

_____

_____

_____

V. Describe why body heat regulation during physical activity should be a primary concern for pregnant exercisers.

_____

_____

_____

_____

VI. List the American College of Sports Medicine's (ACSM) five pregnancy-specific issues to consider when programming prenatal exercise.

1._____

2._____

3._____

4._____

5._____

VII. List the Society of Obstetricians and Gynaecologists of Canada (SOGC) and the Canadian Society for Exercise Physiology (CSEP) recommendations for exercise and the postpartum period.

1._____

_____

2._____

_____

3._____

_____

4._____

_____

5._____

_____

6._____

_____

VIII. Explain the benefits of aquatic exercise for pregnant clients.

_____

_____

_____

_____

IX. Provide a theoretical cause for posterior pelvic pain during pregnancy and give exercise recommendations that may benefit prenatal clients with this condition.

_____

_____

_____

_____

X. *Describe the etiology of diastasis recti during pregnancy.*

_____

_____

_____

_____

XI. *List the six risk factors that predispose a woman to postpartum stress urinary incontinence (SUI).*

1._____

2._____

3._____

4._____

5._____

6._____

XII. *List six benefits of a prenatal Kegel exercise regimen.*

1._____

2._____

3._____

4._____

5._____

6._____

XIII. Define "the maternity blues" and discuss possible reasons for its occurrence in new mothers.

_____

_____

_____

_____

_____

_____

XIV. List four benefits of postpartum exercise.

1._____

2._____

3._____

4._____

XV. Describe the relationship between training the pelvic floor and strengthening the core musculature and give recommendations for the progression of these exercises for the postnatal client.

_____

_____

_____

_____

_____

_____

_____

Practice What You Know

Create as many modified exercises as possible in the recumbent and semirecumbent positions for use with pregnant clients who have progressed into their second and third trimesters and still want to strengthen their abdominal muscles.

Appendix A

Certification Information Guide

I. Purpose

The purpose of this information is to provide you with insight into the American Council on Exercise's (ACE) certification process. By understanding how the examination is developed, you can better prepare for the exam. ACE follows the highest standards for professional and occupational certification tests, taking measures to uphold validity, reliability, and fairness for all candidates in our examinations.

II. How is the Exam developed?

The ACE certification examinations are developed by ACE and volunteer committees of experts in the field(s) in cooperation with CASTLE Worldwide, Inc., an independent testing agency. The exam development process involves the following steps:

A. Job Analysis

A committee of experts in the fitness field thoroughly analyzes the job requirements and develops an outline of the knowledge and skills necessary to perform the job competently.

B. Validation Study

A research survey is then conducted to determine if the job analysis is valid. This survey is sent to thousands of randomly selected fitness professionals for input and validation. The final outcome is the *Exam Content Outline*. (See Appendix B in the *ACE Advanced Health & Fitness Specialist Manual*).

C. Item Writing

A national panel of experts develops questions for the exam. Questions are tied specifically to the validated *Exam Content Outline,* which resulted from the job analysis. All questions are also referenced to an acceptable text or document and further validated for importance, criticalness, and relevance. CASTLE then reviews the questions for the degree to which they adhere to testing guidelines.

D. Exam Construction

The questions are then reviewed in detail one more time by the examination committee before being placed on the final exam forms.

E. Cut Score Determination

Once the final exam is constructed, the exam committee rates the difficulty of each question and the passing point is then determined by statistical analysis of the committee ratings. This analysis adjusts for variability in the ratings and gives benefit to the test candidate.

F. Continual Exam Evaluation

Once the exam process is completed, continual evaluation and analysis of each question helps to ensure validity. The examination is revised each year with items being reworked or replaced. Approximately every five years, the exam-development process begins again with a new job analysis.

III. How is the Exam administered?

An independent testing agency is used to administer all ACE examinations to ensure exam security, integrity, and the elimination of bias. Be assured that all of the policies that ACE follows concerning exam administration are required to maintain these high standards.

IV. Who is eligible to take the Exam?

The ACE Advanced Health & Fitness Specialist Certification Exam is available to those who meet the following prerequisites:
- You must be at least 18 years of age.
- You must hold current adult CPR certification.
- You must have 300 hours of work experience designing and implementing programs for apparently healthy individuals, as documented by a qualified professional.
- You must have a four-year (bachelor's) degree in exercise science or a related field; or a current ACE Personal Trainer certification; or an NCCA-accredited certification.

American Council on Exercise
4851 Paramount Drive
San Diego, CA 92123
(800) 825-3636
www.acefitness.org

Appendix B

Answer Key
Chapter 1

Role and Scope of Practice for the Advanced Health & Fitness Specialist

Expand Your Knowledge

I. (1) Those who are at risk for chronic disease or dysfunction; (2) Those who have borderline health conditions that can be reversed or maintained with a progressive health and fitness program; (3) Those with newly diagnosed metabolic or orthopedic conditions and who are in need of professional health and fitness guidance; (4) Those with chronic metabolic or orthopedic conditions and in need of continued health and fitness guidance; (5) Post-rehabilitation patients following discharge from an outpatient rehabilitation program

II. (a) physician; (b) 20 minutes; (c) Primary; (d) chemoprophylaxis; (e) drug; (f) Physical Activity Readiness Medical Exam Form (PARmed-X); (g) absolute; (h) verbally review

III. (1) Pre-exercise assessment report; (2) Monthly progress reports using a summary of daily SOAP notes; (3) Post-exercise program summary of progress; (4) Written and/or verbal communication on complications or emergency situations

IV. (a) PERF; (b) PHYS; (c) PERF; (d) PHYS; (e) PSYC; (f) PERF; (g) PSYC; (h) PERF

V. (1) Create a written promotional plan; (2) Market trainer to trainer; (3) Offer free educational seminars; (4) Write; (5) Volunteer; (6) Create packages; (7) Utilize ACE resources

Show What You Know

Since Marcia will be spending only two hours per week working with you, it is important to establish a comprehensive fitness plan for the remaining time away from the one-on-one training sessions. A home exercise program for Marcia would help optimize her health and wellness. Using information-gathering techniques, you could modify Marcia's program when necessary and enable the successful completion of the agreed-upon goals and objectives. This approach teaches Marcia to be accountable for her own behavioral modification and provides her with the necessary tools and support to facilitate positive change.

Chapter 2

Working With Clients With Health Challenges

Expand Your Knowledge

I. (a). The ACE-AHFS should have frank discussions about a client's disease by identifying the client's knowledge base of the disease, its signs and symptoms, the expectations of its progression or regression with a fitness program, and any concerns the client may have regarding how this disease impacts his or her life. (b) (1) Physical activity stimulates the secretion of many hormones, including growth hormone, norepinephrine, epinephrine, and glucagon. Glucagon is secreted to convert stored glycogen into glucose, which improves the efficiency of insulin for several hours after each session. Norepinephrine and epinephrine are released in the brain and throughout the body to elevate mood during and immediately after exercise. With regular exercise, the body seeks to continue staying active, sustaining a positive feedback loop. (2) Regular exercise leads to improved sleep quality and duration, which also contributes to the release of nocturnal, reparative substances, including growth hormone, insulin-like growth factors, and melatonin. Consequently, adequate restorative sleep leads to improved mental clarity and increased creativity. (3) There is a sense of accomplishment and heightened satisfaction at reaching small goals with each exercise session and intermediate goals at set intervals. (c) Empathy is the ability to express emotion for another person. It is sometimes described as being able to "walk in another's shoes," or vicariously living through another's experience. Sympathy involves concordance or agreement with the other's feelings. In other words, the ACE-AHFS needs to agree with a client's emotional reaction to be sympathetic, but does not need to agree to be empathetic. (d) (1) The physical costs of starting a program include the discomfort associated with muscle soreness and temporary fatigue with activity. (2) The mental costs include a change of perspective with regards to self-image. (3) The emotional costs include the self-consciousness of being in a fitness facility, working out in front of other people, or having to choose a workout over other social activities. (4) The monetary costs can include gym membership or equipment, clothing and footwear, and trainer fees.

II.   (a) EX; (b) IN; (c) EX; (d) EX; (e) EX; (f) IN; (g) IN; (h) EX; (i) EX; (j) EX

III. (1) Avoiding stress—When dealing with an avoidable negative stressor, such as a person or a place, limiting interactions with that person or place will decrease the total stress load. (2) Altering the context of the stress—Most stressors are potentially manageable. By balancing the schedule to reflect positive and negative stress activities, a person can reduce his or her total stress load. (3) Controlling reactions to stressors—Learning to separate one's feelings and reactions to a stressor. Being able to recognize negative internal cues and separate from them will make it easier to practice new positive behaviors. In other words, if a person cannot control the stressors, he or she can control the reaction to them. (4) Adaptation—This step

involves resiliency to challenges. Physical resiliency comes from a well-balanced diet, adequate sleep and relaxation, and regular exercise, whereas mental resiliency comes from the ability to look at each situation positively and being able to identify opportunities when problems arise. Emotional resiliency is the ability to reject negative thinking and have a sense of humor when situations do not go as well as planned or as expected.

IV. (1) Recognizing the presence of a strong feeling in the interview setting; (2) Pausing to imagine how the other might be feeling; (3) Stating the perception of that feeling (e.g., "I can see you are frustrated."); (4) Legitimizing the feeling (e.g., "That is understandable."); (5) Respecting the effort to cope with the problem; (6) Offering support and partnership (e.g., "Let's see what we can do to improve…")

V.   (1) Alcohol—Long-term, heavy usage of alcohol, or even occasional binge drinking, leads to altered end-organ function with age. The effects are amplified when the alcohol usage is commenced at an early age. The most commonly reported disease associated with heavy alcohol use is liver disease. Because the liver produces nearly all of the non-cellular blood proteins, every tissue in the body becomes more fragile with long-term heavy alcohol consumption. Alcohol consumption leads to decreased reaction time, decreased motor coordination, and impaired memory at the time of usage. (2) Caffeine—A xanthine compound, caffeine is part of a group of central nervous system stimulants that also includes nicotine. When consumed in moderation, caffeine can lead to moderate improvements in executive tasks and motor coordination. However, when consumed in excess, it can lead to nervousness, insomnia, and symptoms that parallel panic and/or heart attacks. It can be an addictive substance for susceptible persons, leading to symptoms of withdrawal if completely and suddenly removed.

VI. (1) Typically, a patient sees a physician with a primary concern. A question that an ACE-AHFS can ask is, "What is your primary goal in starting an exercise program?" A client may state that he or she is interested in weight loss, increased flexibility, improved general fitness, or sport-specific improvements. The ACE-AHFS can use this information for fitness programming. (2) For the client starting a fitness program, sometimes there will be a sentinel event, such as a heart attack or recent onset of sciatica. To better understand the underlying motive for making lifestyle modifications, the ACE-AHFS may consider asking questions about the client's current function and how the recent event has affected him or her, if he or she has any feelings of distress about the sentinel event, and/or what his or her fears may be. (3) An ACE-AHFS who has some training in the basic pathophysiology of diseases may want to take note of the client's other known medical problems. Perhaps more important to the program development are the client's past exercise habits, his or her interest in those activities, whether the program was successful at achieving the fitness goals, and whether that same type of program or goal is believed to be feasible at this time. (4) In the medical setting, a patient is asked about allergies and medications. These details are also important information for the ACE-AHFS, as they can be helpful in the event that an accident requires intervention by emergency personnel. (5) The family history offers a glimpse at a person's genetic predisposition, and the social history provides information about the personal habits, occupation, and environmental modifiers that potentially affect function. It is worth asking about the activity habits of a person's family or social network, as this information helps to identify potential areas of modification needed in the client's fitness goals. (6) Most complete medical exams include questions regarding constitution (fever, chills, weight gain or loss), and a systematic review of the different organ systems. For the ACE-AHFS, this may be a good time to allow the client to talk about anything he or she might have otherwise forgotten during the intake. (7) A complete medical examination would encompass a general overview of the anatomy and biomechanical function within the scope of the practitioner's practice. For the ACE-AHFS, an initial evaluation will require an assessment of the client's exercise attitudes and physical-activity history prior to starting the first workout or attempting physical-fitness testing. (8) This portion of the program requires professional judgment, assimilating the information acquired into a summary of the state of health of a client. For the ACE-AHFS, it may be worth commenting on specific aspects of fitness, such as strength, endurance, balance, and flexibility with respect to the client's stated goals. (9) Physicians will typically list elements to be addressed with end goals specified. The ACE-AHFS can list short-term and intermediate- to long-term goals based on measurable results (e.g., "Improve walking speed on treadmill from 3 mph to 3.5 mph, improve duration from 10 minutes to 20 minutes in 15 sessions over four weeks. The client would like to be able to complete a 5K walk with her daughter in six months time.").

Show What You Know

It is important to separate the signs and symptoms of the disease from Bob's sense of self. A focus on functional gains and separating Bob from his disease can dramatically impact his outlook in a positive way. During the initial interview and throughout the program, it is important to ask how Bob feels, preferably as an open-ended question.

Depending on his personality, a series of questions may be needed to follow up on the first response. It would be helpful to have Bob recall a functional gain, a limitation, and a moment when he felt good with the circumstances. This verbalization would help him reinforce a positive image of the fitness activity relative to his function and further help with program progression. By allowing Bob to openly talk about his feelings, you offer a way to discharge the negative impact of the health challenge prior to the workout, allowing for more productivity during the exercise session. However, if you determine that Bob has been traumatized by the sudden onset of the disease process, he may need a referral to a psychologist for coping skills.

Chapter 3

Communication Strategies and Behavior Change

Expand Your Knowledge

I. (a) 7; (b) 5; (c) 6; (d) 10; (e) 9; (f) 2; (g) 4; (h) 1; (i) 8; (j) 3

II. (1) When the ACE-AHFS and the client have significantly different backgrounds, the ACE-AHFS must spend extra time and energy learning about the client. As he or she gains experience with a given population, the ACE-AHFS will become more adept at establishing rapport with clients from that group. However, the ACE-AHFS must never generalize or stereotype. (2) Clients grappling with depression or anxiety may tend to focus on negative information and not hear the positive. When working with clients with mood disorders, the ACE-AHFS must be sure to phrase information in a positive, supportive way. (3) The ACE-AHFS should use language clients can understand and try to meet clients' need for information without "talking down" to them, using technical jargon, or providing too much information. (4) The largest barrier to quality communication is a lack of effective listening, which is likely to occur when either party feels rushed and distracted and does not pay attention to what the other person is saying. Cultivating the ability to focus one's attention mindfully is a good antidote to stress and improves communication. (5) Initial meetings between the ACE-AHFS and clients should occur in a comfortable, quiet, private space. Such space is not always readily available in fitness centers. In this case, fitness-center personnel should create a quiet space where clients do not feel like they will be overheard.

III. (1) People in the precontemplation stage have no intention of becoming more active. They do not exercise and they do not plan to start. They may be unaware that a sedentary lifestyle is risky, or, if they are aware of the risk, feel powerless to begin exercising. They may deny the extent or seriousness of the problem and use defensive strategies when others suggest that a sedentary lifestyle is dangerous. Effective strategies for working with a precontemplator include uncovering misinformation, providing education regarding exercise benefits and the dangers of inactivity, and discussing barriers to exercise. The client must make the decision to become active, and the ACE-AHFS can help to facilitate this decision by listening carefully to clients and addressing their concerns. (2) People in the contemplation stage are sedentary, but are thinking about becoming more active in the near future. They are still weighing the pros and cons of becoming active and are thinking about whether to exercise regularly. They may be wondering how to begin. The ACE-AHFS can help contemplators strengthen the pros and weaken the cons of exercise by providing additional information on exercise benefits and addressing the client's concerns about adopting a program of regular physical activity. A contemplator may be more likely to sign on to an exercise program that is perceived to be simple and convenient. (3) People in the preparation stage have decided to become more active and are preparing to begin. They may have signed up for a class, made an appointment to work with a personal trainer, bought some exercise equipment, or joined a fitness center. People in preparation believe in the benefits of regular physical activity, but may have unrealistic expectations for the changes they hope to achieve by exercising. Their plans may be overly ambitious. They may underestimate the time and energy their exercise plans will take, as well as potential exercise barriers. The ACE-AHFS can help people in the preparation stage become successful by working with them to set well-defined, realistic goals and designing convenient exercise programs tailored to clients' abilities and lifestyles. Exercise history can provide insight to what has worked and what has not worked in the past for a specific client. (4) People in the action stage have begun exercising regularly, but have not yet maintained their exercise behavior for six months. Because exercise is a difficult habit to maintain, people in the action stage continue to benefit from sustained support from, and contact with, the ACE-AHFS. Clients in the action stage continue to appreciate information on exercise benefits, strategies to best achieve health and fitness goals, and help with making regular physical activity a lifelong habit. (5) People in the maintenance stage have been exercising regularly for at least six months. These clients may seek professional advice on modifying their exercise programs to better address their health and fitness goals or to add variety to their exercise programs.

IV. (1) *Educate clients about the importance of psychological health.* Clients commonly seek the advice of fitness professionals for physical concerns, but many do not realize that physical activity may improve psychological well-being. Engaging in regular self-care, including physical activity, helps people maintain or improve emotional balance. Poor psychological health is associated with many health risks. Similarly, clients with physical health problems often experience psychological problems as well. (2) *Include psychological benefits in health and fitness goals.* Once clients understand that regular physical activity can help reduce feelings of stress and improve mood, they can be encouraged to include these psychological benefits in their health and fitness goals. When clients are consciously aware of the psychological benefits that may result from their exercise programs, they are more likely to experience them, and to figure out what kinds of exercise work best for them. (3) *Recommend effective activities.* Some clients may already understand what types of activities give them the greatest stress-reduction benefits. In general, moderately vigorous activities tend to be effective and well-tolerated. The ACE-AHFS should remember, however, that beginners may become too fatigued by overly vigorous options. Therefore, the ACE-AHFS should ask clients about activities they enjoy and then incorporate these into program design whenever possible, as personal preferences have an important influence on intrinsic motivation and adherence. (4) *Measure mood changes with exercise.* Some fitness professionals measure mood before and after exercise sessions using a questionnaire such as the exercise-induced feeling inventory. Responses can be compared before and after several weeks of participation in an exercise program.

V. (a learned helplessness; (b) extrinsically motivated; intrinsically motivated; (c) behavior chain; (d) Self-efficacy;

(e) motor learning; (f) perception; (g) 10%; (h) exercise-specific self-efficacy

VI.(1) Remind beginners that it takes time and practice to improve motor skills. (2) Introduce a new skill slowly and clearly. (3) Adapt teaching methods to each client's learning style when possible. (4) Allow clients the opportunity for focused practice. (5) Give helpful feedback.

Show What You Know

Cindy most likely suffers from learned helplessness, in that she believes she is helpless in, or has little power or control over, certain situations. In conversations with Cindy, the ACE-AHFS should try to help her view the exercise program as being achievable and under her control. If Cindy starts explaining why the program will not work, the ACE-AHFS should listen carefully and try to design a program that is as simple and convenient as possible. In addition, the ACE-AHFS should help Cindy view challenges that arise as a function of controllable and changeable factors, rather than personal failings.

Chapter 4

Professional Relationships and Business Strategies

Expand Your Knowledge

I. (1) Obtaining medical clearance for a specific exercise program; (2) Obtaining recommendations regarding an exercise program; (3) Determining the physical limitations of an exercise program; (4) Introducing the ACE-AHFS and his or her services; (5) Clarifying questions on the client's health; (6) Obtaining special considerations related to the client's health (e.g., a chronic disease such as diabetes or hypertension); (7) Providing progress reports on the exercise program, or receiving health status updates; (8) Establishing rapport with a potential referral source

II. 1) Health history; (2) Medical releases; (3) Informed consent; (4) Liability waiver; (5) Training contracts; (6) Correspondence sheets; (7) Initial assessments; (8) Additional assessments; (9) Training progressions; (10) SOAP notes

III. (1) The initial portion of the SOAP note consists of subjective observations. These are symptoms verbalized by the client or by a significant other. These subjective observations include the client's descriptions of pain or discomfort or a multitude of other descriptions of any dysfunction, discomfort, or illness. (2) The next part of the format is the objective observation, which includes symptoms that can actually be measured, seen, heard, touched, or felt. Objective observations include vital signs such as resting heart rate, blood pressure, body weight, percent body fat, waist circumference, and the results of any other related tests or evaluations. (3) The assessment follows the objective observations and is a statement of the client's condition. In some cases, this statement may be clear, such as "moderately obese." In other instances, an assessment may not be as clear and can include several possibilities. The word "statement" is used quite intentionally in this description. In the medical field, the assessment is usually a "diagnosis," but the scope of practice of an ACE-AHFS does not include making medical diagnoses. Therefore, any reference to a diagnosis should be avoided. (4) The last part of the SOAP note is the plan. The plan may include further fitness testing or other diagnostic testing. This is where a referral to another healthcare professional would be noted. This is also the section where an ACE-AHFS would record his or her appropriate plan in terms of exercise, nutrition, and adherence strategies.

IV. (1) Timeliness of the communication: Tardy communication places the physician in a position in which he or she is uninformed of what other team members are doing. This decreases the chance that the physician will send the ACE-AHFS another referral. If the ACE-AHFS knows the client has scheduled an appointment with the physician that will take place before he or she can send a letter, the ACE-AHFS should consider calling the physician's office to give a brief report on any findings and recommendations. It is important to keep written notes in the client's file that detail any phone conversations with the client or physician. The ACE-AHFS should always be prompt with all replies and type them in a professional manner. (2) Lack of understanding of team member roles: Because physicians generally are unfamiliar with the role that the ACE-AHFS can play in the healthcare team, the ACE-AHFS may need to educate physicians on what he or she has to offer. The method of doing so may include a phone call to let the physician know that he or she can use the ACE-AHFS as a resource for any fitness-related questions. Other means that the ACE-AHFS can use to introduce him- or herself to the physician include explaining his or her areas of expertise in all referral letters, personally visiting the physician's office, and sending pertinent articles on different aspects of personal training and exercise. (3) Unclear expectations: The ACE-AHFS must be sure to understand what a physician expects, and then strive to deliver it. The ACE-AHFS must be clear about what he or she has to offer the healthcare team, how to utilize that expertise, and when it is appropriate to refer an individual to a member of the allied healthcare team. It is also important to let the physician know what kind of results clients can expect so that they may provide reinforcement when they see the client. (4) Reaching beyond the scope of practice: If the ACE-AHFS does not know an answer or cannot help an individual, he or she must be willing to admit it and refer the client to the appropriate member of the healthcare team.

V. (a) confidential; private; (b) password; (c) Marketing; (d) competitive advantage; (e) Word of mouth; (f) eight to 10; 20; (g) cancellation policies; late fees; (h) mainstream community; home-based exercise

VI. 1) Have legal professionals review all documentation used with clients. (2) Allow clients to have appropriate time to read and sign all training documentation. (3) Verbally answer questions when necessary. (4) Store all documents securely for as long as is required by the state's statute of limitations. (5) Be sure to carry sufficient liability insurance for ultimate protection against liability. (6) Use a legally reviewed, standardized waiver form with all clients.

VII. (1) Sole proprietorship: This type of business is owned and operated by one individual. Such owners have total control over business activities and forming a sole proprietorship is easy and inexpensive. Profits are considered personal income, which makes tax preparation simple. The disadvantage of a sole proprietorship is that the personal liability of the proprietor is not protected. If the business cannot pay its creditors, the ACE-AHFS may be forced to use his or her own money to cover the debts. Personal and business funds are one account, not two different accounts. There is also a limited source of funds and individuals pay a higher marginal tax rate. (2) Partnership: In a partnership, two or more people agree to operate a business and share profits and losses. A partnership is taxed like a sole proprietorship. There are two main types of partnerships: general partnerships and limited partnerships. (3) Corporation: A corporation is a legal entity recognized by the state, the assets and liabilities of which are separate from its owners. The advantages of a corporation are the limited liability, the ease of transfer of ownership, and the external sources of funds. Disadvantages of a corporation include double taxation, which means that both income and dividends are taxed. Other disadvantages are the costliness of formation and the disclosure of information. There are two subgroups of the corporation: the S-Corp and the limited liability corporation (LLC).

Show What You Know

I. S—executive business manager; interested in lowering blood pressure, alleviating stress, losing 30 lb (14 kg), and feeling better; can commit to three workout sessions a week plus walking to and from work twice per week; O—52-year-old female; body weight 165 lb (74 kg); body fat 28%; and diagnosed hypertension; A—52-year-old overweight, busy executive experiencing work-related stress; P—balanced exercise program including aerobic exercise, strength training, and stretching; focus on aerobic exercise and relaxation during stretching as a way to minimize stress and combat hypertension; discuss and implement healthy eating plan that addresses achieving good nutrition within a hectic schedule

Chapter 5

Nutritional Considerations for an Active Lifestyle

Expand Your Knowledge

I. (1) Vitamins are organic, non-caloric micronutrients that are essential for normal physiologic function. With the exceptions of vitamin K, biotin, and vitamin D, vitamins must be consumed through food. Minerals are inorganic substances that serve roles that range from regulating enzyme activity and maintaining acid-base balance to assisting with strength and growth. Unlike

vitamins, many minerals are found in the body as well as in food. (2) Thiamin, riboflavin, niacin, pantothenic acid, folate, vitamin B6, vitamin B12, biotin, and vitamin C are the water-soluble vitamins. They are soluble in water and are cofactors of enzymes involved in metabolism. With the exception of vitamins B6 and B12, water-soluble vitamins cannot be stored in the body and are readily excreted in urine. Vitamins A, D, E, and K are the fat-soluble vitamins. Often found in fat-containing foods and stored in the liver or adipose tissue until needed, fat-soluble vitamins closely associate with fat. Unlike water-soluble vitamins, fat-soluble vitamins can be stored in the body for extended periods of time. (3) A monosaccharide is the simplest form of sugar. Monosaccharides are usually found joined together as di-, oligo-, or polysaccharides. Three monosaccharides found in nature can be absorbed and utilized by humans—glucose, galactose, and fructose. An oligosaccharide is a chain of about three to 10 or fewer simple sugars. Fructooligosaccharides, a category of oligosaccharides that are mostly indigestible, may help to relieve constipation, improve triglyceride levels, and decrease the production of foul-smelling digestive by-products. (4) Amino acids that bind together to form proteins that are made in the body are termed nonessential amino acids. Eight to 10 essential amino acids have carbon skeletons that humans cannot make and so must be consumed in the diet. Generally, animal products contain all of the essential amino acids in amounts proportional to need and are called complete proteins. Usually, proteins in plant foods do not contain all of the essential amino acids in amounts proportional to need and are called incomplete proteins. (5) Mechanical digestion is the process of chewing, swallowing, and propelling food through the gastrointestinal tract. Chemical digestion includes the addition of enzymes that break down nutrients. (6) The esophageal sphincter, also known as the cardiac sphincter, prevents food and stomach acid from splashing back into the esophagus from the stomach, while the pyloric sphincter separates the stomach from the small intestine. (7) When more calories are consumed than expended, an individual is in positive energy balance, which is necessary during times of growth such as in infancy, childhood, and pregnancy. Otherwise, positive energy balance results in weight gain. When more calories are expended than consumed, an individual is in negative energy balance, which is necessary for weight loss.

II. (1) Mostly whole grains, as opposed to refined sugars; (2) Ample nutrient-dense dark green and orange vegetables such as broccoli and carrots, rather than disproportionate amounts of starchy vegetables like white potatoes and corn, which contain fewer vitamins and minerals; (3) A variety of fruits, preferably from the whole-food sources, as opposed to fruit juices; (4) Oils in moderation, with an emphasis on mono- or polyunsaturated fats instead of trans or saturated fats; (5) Low- or nonfat milk products, as opposed to regular whole-milk products; (6) Lean meat and bean products, instead of higher fat meats such as regular (75 to 80% lean) ground beef or chicken with the skin

III. (1) The Estimated Average Requirement (EAR) for carbohydrates is 100 grams (about seven servings) for non-pregnant, non-lactating adults and children; 135 grams (about seven servings) for pregnant women; and 160 grams (about 11 servings) for lactating women. The American Dietetic Association (ADA) recommends that athletes consume between 6 and 10 grams of carbohydrates per kilogram of body weight (3 to 5 g/lb) per day to maintain blood glucose levels during exercise and to replenish muscle glycogen stores. (2) Soluble fiber helps prevent heart disease and stroke by binding bile and cholesterol; diabetes by

slowing glucose absorption; and constipation by holding moisture in stools and softening them. Insoluble fiber reduces constipation and lowers the risk of hemorrhoids and diverticulosis by adding bulk to the feces and reducing transit time in the colon. Increased consumption of both soluble and insoluble fiber helps to increase satiety and may lead to decreased caloric intake. As a result, a diet high in fiber may help promote weight loss. (3) GI ranks carbohydrates based on their blood glucose response: high-GI foods break down rapidly, causing a large spike in glucose levels, while low-GI foods are digested more slowly and cause smaller blood glucose–level increases. A diet based on the consumption of high-GI carbohydrates promotes greater glycogen storage following strenuous exercise, which could benefit performance. On the other hand, a low-GI eating plan may be better for weight loss and for people with the metabolic syndrome or diabetes.

IV. (1) Fats serve the functions of insulation, support of the cell structure, nerve transmission, vitamin absorption, and hormone production. (2) Eicosanoids are oxygenated fatty acids that the body uses to signal cellular responses. Both omega-3 and omega-6 fatty acids are used to make eicosanoids. (3) Eicosanoids made from omega-6 tend to cause inflammation and increase blood pressure and blood clotting. Eicosanoids made from omega-3 have the opposite effects, as they reduce blood clotting, dilate blood vessels, and reduce inflammation. This balancing act between omega-6 and omega-3 is essential for maintaining normal circulation and other essential processes. Reducing consumption of omega-6 fatty acids and increasing consumption of omega-3 fatty acids may lower chronic disease risk. (4) Trans fat is a heart-damaging fat that increases LDL cholesterol even more than saturated fat. The ACE-AHFS should encourage clients to check food labels and look on the ingredients list for "partially hydrogenated" oil to determine if a food contains even small amounts of trans fat. If so, they should avoid that food.

V. (1) The average person requires 0.8 to 1.0 g/kg of body weight per day (0.4 to 0.5 g/lb). The American Dietetic Association, Dietitians of Canada, and the American College of Sports Medicine recommend that endurance athletes consume about 1.2 to 1.4 g/kg (0.5 to 0.6 g/lb), whereas strength-trained athletes should consume up to 1.6 to 1.7 g/kg (0.7 to 0.8 g/lb). However, the Institute of Medicine suggests that 0.8 g/kg (0.3 g/lb) of bodyweight per day is appropriate for athletes. (2) Protein is involved in formation of the brain, nervous system, blood, muscle, skin, and hair, as well as the transport of iron, vitamins, minerals, fats, and oxygen. Proteins are also the key to acid-base and fluid balance. Proteins form enzymes, which speed up chemical reactions to milliseconds that might otherwise take years. Antibodies that the body makes to fight infection are made from proteins. In situations of energy deprivation, the body can break down proteins for energy. (3) Amino-acid composition—proteins containing all essential amino acids in amounts proportional to need have a higher biological value); cooking and preparation—cooking methods that destroy essential amino acids decrease biological value; and vitamin and mineral content—foods missing certain critical nutrients have drastically decreased biological values

VI. (a) 7; (b) 5; (c) 8; (d) 2; (e) 1; (f) 3; (g) 4; (h) 6

VII. The sympathetic nervous system acts to increase blood and oxygen supply to the working muscles. It does this by increasing heart rate and by shunting blood away from the gastrointestinal system (by constricting the peripheral arteries) and to the working muscles (by dilating the arteries to muscle and liver). The sympathetic nervous system also triggers the release

of several exercise hormones. Epinephrine is released from the adrenal medulla. It increases blood glucose by inducing the breakdown of liver and muscle glycogen (glycogenolysis). Epinephrine also increases glucose by decreasing the release of insulin from the pancreas. Glucocorticoids, which are steroid hormones including cortisol, are released from the adrenal cortex. The glucocorticoids stimulate glucose production from amino-acid building blocks (gluconeogenesis). The net result is more glucose in the bloodstream and thus more glucose directed to the muscles for energy release as ATP.

VIII. (a) phosphagen; (b) ATP; energy; (c) Lactic acid; (d) oxidative phosphorylation; (e) dehydration; (f) hyponatremia; (g) Gastric emptying; (h) three hours; (i) 1.5 g/kg of body weight; two hours

IX. (1) Use thirst to determine fluid needs. Advise clients to drink when they are thirsty and stop drinking when they feel hydrated. (2) Aim for a 1:1 ratio of fluid replacement to fluid lost in sweat. Ideally, people should consume the same amount of fluid as is lost in sweat. Clients can check their hydration status by comparing pre- and post-exercise weight. Perfect hydration occurs when no weight is lost or gained during exercise. Another simple way to determine adequate hydration status is to check urine color. Individuals will know that they are adequately hydrated when their urine is clear or pale yellow. (3) Measure fluid amounts. When exercisers know how much they are actually drinking, they may be able to better assess if they are consuming appropriate amounts. (4) Drink fluids with sodium during prolonged exercise sessions. If an exercise session lasts longer than two hours or an athlete is participating in an event that stimulates heavy sodium loss (defined as more than 3 to 4 grams of sodium), experts recommend that the athlete drink a sports drink that contains elevated levels of sodium. Alternatively, exercisers can consume extra sodium with meals and snacks prior to a lengthy exercise session or a day of extensive physical activity. (5) Drink carbohydrate-containing sports drinks to reduce fatigue. With prolonged exercise, muscle glycogen stores become depleted and blood glucose becomes a primary fuel source. To maintain performance levels and prevent fatigue, clients should consume drinks and snacks that provide about 30 to 60 grams of rapidly absorbed carbohydrate for every hour of training.

X.

Factors Affecting Resting Metabolic Rate

Factor	RMR	Comments
Age	↓	Likely due to a loss of lean body mass
Body Temperature	↑	Seen with temperature extremes: fever and hypothermia (shivering)
Caffeine and Tobacco	↑	These stimulants increase metabolism
Gender	↑↓	Males tend to have more lean body mass
Nervous System Activity	↑	The "fight or flight" hormone norepinephrine can increase RMR
Nutritional Status	↓	Reduced calorie intake can depress RMR
Pregnancy	↑	Periods of growth require extra energy expenditure
Thyroid Hormones	↑↓	People with too much thyroid hormone (hyperthyroidism) have increased RMR, and those with not enough (hypothyroidism) have decreased RMR

Note: ↑ = Increase;   ↓ = Decrease;   ↑↓= Variable

Source: Modified from Wardlaw, G.M., Hampl, J.S., & DiSilvestro, R.A. (2004). *Perspectives in Nutrition* (6th ed.). New York: McGraw-Hill.

XI. (1) Take warning signs seriously. If an ACE-AHFS believes that someone may have an eating disorder, he or she should share those concerns in an open, direct, and sensitive manner, keeping in mind the following "don'ts" when confronting someone with a suspected eating or exercise disorder: Don't oversimplify, diagnose, become the person's therapist, provide exercise advice without first helping the individual get professional help, or get into a battle of wills if the person denies having a problem. (2) Deemphasize weight. An ACE-AHFS should not weigh at-risk clients and should eliminate comments about weight, especially with those individuals believed to be at risk for an eating disorder. (3) Do not assume that reducing body fat or weight will improve performance. (4) Help other fitness professionals recognize the signs of eating disorders and how to be prepared to address them. (5) Provide accurate information about weight, weight loss, body composition, nutrition, and sports performance. (6) Emphasize the health risks of low weight, especially for female athletes with menstrual irregularities (in which case referral to a physician, preferably one who specializes in eating disorders, is warranted). (7) Avoid making any derogatory comments about weight or body composition to, or about, anyone. (8) Do not curtail athletic performance and gym privileges for an athlete or client who is found to have eating problems unless it is medically necessary to do so. (9) Strive to promote a positive self-image and self-esteem in clients and athletes.

Chapter 6

Coronary Artery Disease

Expand Your Knowledge

I. (1) Phase I cardiac rehabilitation is the in-patient phase that includes teaching and low-level hospital-based ambulatory exercise, while Phase II is the early hospital discharge phase of rehabilitation and includes medically monitored exercise and more concentrated risk-factor education. (2) Atherosclerosis is a disease affecting arterial blood vessels. It is a chronic inflammatory response in the walls of arteries, in large part due to the deposition of lipoproteins. Atherosclerosis is essentially caused by the formation of multiple plaques within the arteries. Atherogenesis is the process of the development of these plaques, which involves the infiltration, retention, and oxidation of LDL cholesterol in the arterial intima, development of fatty streaks, and the calcification of atherosclerotic plaques. (3) Angina that occurs regularly with activity, upon awakening, or at other predictable times is termed stable angina and is associated with high-grade narrowing of the coronary arteries. Unstable angina is angina that changes in intensity, character, or frequency. Unstable angina may precede myocardial infarction and requires urgent medical attention.

II. (1) The exercise ECG test is a graded exercise treadmill test with electrocardiographic recording. The test is considered "positive" if there is a specific standard level of change in the S-T segment component of the ECG. For functional assessment, the test is used primarily to evaluate the patient's symptomology, MET capacity, and training heart-rate response. (2) Radionuclide stress testing involves injecting a radioactive isotope (typically thallium or cardiolyte) into the person's vein, after which an image of the heart becomes visible with a special camera. The radioactive isotopes are absorbed by the normal heart muscle. Nuclear images are obtained in the resting condition and again immediately following exercise. The two sets of images are then compared. During exercise, if a significant blockage in a coronary artery or arteries results in diminished blood flow to a part of the cardiac muscle, this region of the heart will appear as a relative "cold spot" on the nuclear scan, signifying reduced or diminished blood flow. (3)

During stress echocardiography, the sound waves of an ultrasound are used to produce images of the heart at rest and at the peak of exercise. In a heart with normal blood supply, all segments of the left ventricle exhibit enhanced contractions of the heart muscle during peak exercise. Conversely, in the presence of CAD, if a segment of the left ventricle does not receive optimal blood flow during exercise, that segment will demonstrate reduced contractions of the heart muscle relative to the rest of the heart on the exercise echocardiogram. (4) Coronary angiography involves inserting a catheter into the groin area and routing it into the coronary arteries of the heart. This procedure is done for both diagnostic and interventional purposes. A radio contrast agent is passed into the catheter and is visualized on a fluoroscope to evaluate coronary blood flow in the major arteries of the heart. The benefit of this procedure is that while the catheter is inside the heart, the cardiologist can perform a percutaneous coronary angioplasty (PTCA). (5) In CT angiography, computed tomography using a contrast material produces detailed pictures. CT imaging uses special x-ray equipment to produce multiple images and a computer to join them together in cross-sectional views. This new test is able to diagnose CAD. (6) High-resolution cardiovascular magnetic resonance imaging (CMRI) of the arterial wall is emerging as a powerful research technology for characterizing atherosclerotic lesions within carotid arteries and other large vessels. It is able to noninvasively characterize three important aspects of atherosclerotic lesions: size, composition, and biologic activity. It can quantify not only wall and lumen areas and volumes, but also plaque composition. This technique can also be used to characterize the composition of a plaque by differentiating lipid-free regions from lipid-rich and calcified regions. In addition, high-resolution MRI can identify recent intra-plaque hemorrhages. (7) Intravascular ultrasound (IVUS) allows the tomographic measurement of artery lumen area, plaque size, plaque distribution, and to some extent, plaque composition. Because the arterial remodeling and plaque deposition that characterize the early stages of atherosclerotic progression occur without decreases in lumen area, IVUS may be able to detect atherosclerotic disease at an earlier state than coronary angiography. In many cases, IVUS may provide the ability to detect some "angiographically silent" atheromas. (8) Coronary calcification is part of the pathogenesis of atherosclerosis and does not occur in normal vessels. Due to the association between coronary calcification and plaque development, radiographically detected coronary artery calcium (CAC) can provide an estimate of total coronary plaque build-up. Currently, the primary methods for CAC measurement are electron-beam computed tomography (EBCT) and multi-detector computed tomography (MDCT). (9) B-mode ultrasound is a noninvasive imaging modality that employs ultrasound to accurately image the walls of arteries and is a useful tool for evaluating carotid intima-media wall thickness (CIMT). The normal arterial wall consists of three layers: the tunica intima, tunica media, and tunica adventitia. The thickness of the two innermost layers in the carotid artery (the intima and media), or the CIMT, is increasingly used as a surrogate marker for early atherosclerosis. Carotid ultrasound measurements correlate well with histology, and increased CIMT is associated with the presence of vascular risk factors and more advanced atherosclerosis, including coronary artery disease.

III. (1) Improved $\dot{V}O_2$max (aerobic capacity); (2) Lessening of angina symptoms/raising of the ischemic threshold; (3) Modest decreases in body fat, blood pressure, total and LDL cholesterol, non-HDL cholesterol, and triglycerides; (4) Increased HDL cholesterol; (5) Reduction in stress; (6) Control of diabetes mellitus; (7) Improved well-being and self-efficacy

IV. Progressive aerobic endurance exercise is recommended, as long as it is within the individual's exercise tolerance as indicated by the most recent exercise ECG, or is just below the anginal threshold or physician-recommended percent of $\dot{V}O_2$max. Intermittent, shorter-duration exercise on a more frequent basis may be most appropriate in the initial stages of training. Upper-extremity aerobic training may initially exacerbate angina. Avoid breath holding, isometric exercises, or activities where the individual physically exerts to muscular contraction failure. Maintain close observation of anginal symptoms and ensure that the individual understands when to take angina-resolving medications.

V. Discontinue activity and incorporate rest to see if chest discomfort/pain resolves on its own. If there is no relief, the client will self-administer one dose of nitroglycerin, either in tablet or spray form. A tablet will be placed sublingually or between the cheek and gums. If a spray is used, it would be delivered in the same locations. The client will then wait five minutes to see if the chest pain is resolved. If not, a second dose will be administered. He or she will then wait five more minutes and then repeat one more time before calling 911.

VI. (1) Cardiac dysrhythmias produce symptoms including dizziness, lightheadedness, palpitations, and, in rare occurrences, syncope (fainting). (2) MI symptoms may include various combinations of pain in the chest, upper extremity, or jaw, or epigastric discomfort with exertion or at rest. The discomfort associated with acute MI usually lasts at least 20 minutes. Frequently, the discomfort is diffuse, not localized, not positional, not affected by movement of the region, and may be accompanied by shortness of breath, diaphoresis (excessive sweating), nausea, or syncope (fainting). Patients frequently feel suddenly ill. Women often experience different symptoms from men. The most common symptoms of MI in women include shortness of breath, weakness, and fatigue. Approximately one-third of all myocardial infarctions are "silent," without chest pain or other symptoms. (3) Signs and symptoms of restenosis include complaints of general fatigue, reduced exercise tolerance or accelerated heart rate at customary workloads, and any symptoms of chest discomfort or pain.

VII. (1) To optimize the potential for improvement of CAD risk factors and stabilize the disease process, clients should prioritize achieving a total volume of physical activity of 1500 to 2000 kcal or more per week. (2) ACSM recommends that the initial stages of aerobic-conditioning programs for low-risk and stable CAD clients have an exercise intensity of 40 to 50% of heart-rate reserve (i.e., approximately 40 to 50% of $\dot{V}O_2$max), or 2 to 4 METs. Clients who are in the improvement or maintenance stage of conditioning should work at an intensity range of 60 to 85% of heart-rate reserve (60 to 85% of $\dot{V}O_2$max). The majority of CAD clients will do well with 30 to 60 minutes of exercise. For durations of 45 minutes or longer, exercise intensity should be in the moderate range [i.e., 40 to 60% of heart-rate reserve (40 to 60% of $\dot{V}O_2$max)]. (3) Double product is the product of exercise heart rate and systolic blood pressure divided by 100. This expression corresponds to the anginal threshold. Intensive aerobic activities significantly increase heart rate but moderately increase systolic blood pressure, whereas intensive resistance workloads (e.g., resistance training) moderately increase heart rate but cause a more significant rise in systolic blood pressure. Both forms of exercise can dramatically raise the "double product" and therefore raise cardiac workload. (4) Resistance training should be performed: in a rhythmical manner at moderate to slow controlled speed; through a full range of motion, avoiding breath-holding and straining (Valsalva maneuver) by exhaling during the contraction or exertion phase of the lift and inhaling during the relaxation phase; initially alternating between upper- and lower-body work to allow for adequate rest between exercises. The initial resistance workload should allow for, and be limited to, 8–12 repetitions per set for healthy sedentary adults or 10–15 repetitions at a low level of resistance; be limited to a single set performed two days a week; and involve the major muscle groups of the upper and lower extremities. (5) In yogic breathing, the breath is generally drawn through the nose during both inhalation and exhalation. Each breath is intentionally slow and deep with an even distribution, or smoothness, of effort. Lengthening exhalations by using the abdominal muscles to expire more air while breathing through the nose will cause a relaxation response. In addition to reduced stress and mental tension, cardiovascular benefits result from yogic breathing. One of the mechanisms responsible for the mental quiescence experienced with yogic breathing is its stimulation of the parasympathetic nervous system. When fully stimulated by adequate yogic inspiration and expiration, mechanical receptors in pulmonary tissue activate parasympathetic nerves, which transiently reduces mental tension and increases relaxation response. Acute reductions in blood pressure also have resulted from yogic breathing training.

Show What You Know

The ACE-AHFS should follow the exercise guidelines and precautions for all CAD clients. Fred should focus his exercise program on aerobic activity performed at an exercise intensity of 40 to 50% of heart-rate reserve (i.e., approximately 40 to 50% of $\dot{V}O_2$max), or 2 to 4 METs. Of high importance for CABG clients is the avoidance of traditional resistance-training programs with moderate to heavy weights for the first six weeks post-surgery. This will enable the sternum sufficient time to heal from the CABG sternotomy. Graduated upper-extremity range-of-motion exercises and many hatha yoga poses that do not place undue strain on the sternum or upper back are recommended for clients who have had CABG within the previous four to eight weeks.

Chapter 7

Blood Lipid Disorders

Expand Your Knowledge

I. (a) LDL; (b) NHDL; (c) HDL; (d) LDL; (e) VLDL; (f) LDL; (g) NHDL; (h) NHDL; (i) HDL; (j) LDL; (k) VLDL

II.

LDL Cholesterol	mg/dL
Optimal	<100
Near optimal/above optimal	100–129
Borderline high	130–159
High	160–189
Very high	≥190
Total Cholesterol	
Desirable	<200
Borderline high	200–239
High	≥240
HDL Cholesterol	
Low	<40
High	≥60
Triglycerides	
Normal	<150
Borderline high	150–199
High	200–499
Very high	≥500

III. (1) For high-risk individuals, the overall goal remains an LDL level of less than 100 mg/dL. But for people at very high risk, there is a therapeutic option of reducing LDL to under 70 mg/dL. For very-high-risk people whose LDL levels are already below 100 mg/dL, there is also an option to use drug therapy to reach the less-than-70 mg/dL goal. The NCEP defines high-risk individuals as those who have coronary heart disease or disease of the blood vessels to the brain or extremities, diabetes, or two or more risk factors that give them a greater than 20% chance of having a heart attack within 10 years. Very-high-risk individuals are those who have cardiovascular disease together with either multiple risk factors (especially diabetes), or severe and poorly controlled risk factors, or metabolic syndrome. Patients hospitalized for acute coronary syndromes such as heart attack are also at very high risk. (2) For moderately high-risk individuals, the goal is an LDL <130 mg/dL, with a therapeutic option to set a lower LDL goal of <100 mg/dL and to use drug therapy at LDL levels of 100 to 129 mg/dL to reach this lower goal. Moderately high-risk patients are those who have multiple (two or more) risk factors for coronary heart disease together with a 10 to 20% risk of heart attack within 10 years. (3) Low-risk individuals have a 10-year probability of a heart attack of less than 10% and an LDL cholesterol goal of <160 mg/dL.

IV. (1) The core metabolic risk factors are elevated blood triglycerides, low HDL cholesterol, elevated blood pressure, elevated plasma glucose, a prothrombotic state, and a pro-inflammatory state. (2) The root causes of the metabolic syndrome are overweight/obesity, physical inactivity, and genetic factors. (3) Cardiometabolic risk is a broadened view of the metabolic syndrome. It is defined by a merger of the traditional Framingham

CHD risk factors and the metabolic syndrome risk factors. Cardiometabolic risk encompasses a cluster of modifiable risk factors and markers that identify individuals at increased risk of cardiovascular disease and type 2 diabetes. (4) *Bile acid sequestrants (cholestyramine, colestipol, colesevelam):* These agents bind bile acids in the small intestine and cause decreased bile acid absorption, in turn lowering total and LDL cholesterol. *Nicotinic acid (niacin, niaspan, niacor):* Niacin is a water-soluble B vitamin that is very effective in lowering LDL cholesterol and triglycerides, but is especially utilized to increase HDL cholesterol when used in relatively high doses (>1,500 mg/day). *HMG-CoA reductase inhibittors (also known as statins, which include lovastatin, pravastatin, simvastatin, fluvastatin, atorvastatin, rosuvastatin, and pitavastatin in Japan):* These drugs effectively lower LDL cholesterol by interfering with cholesterol synthesis. They are competitive inhibitors of HMG-CoA reductase, the enzyme responsible for the rate-limiting step in the cholesterol biosynthetic pathway. They also block the formation of mevalonic acid and decrease intracellular cholesterol synthesis. *Combination nicotinic acid and statin drugs:* Advicor® and Simcor® are combination drugs that combine in one pill various combinations of niaspan and lovastatin (Advicor) and niaspan and simvastatin (Simcor). *Fibrates (gemfibrozil, fenofibrate):* Gemfibrozil and fenofibrate primarily lower triglycerides and, to a lesser extent, increase HDL cholesterol by reducing VLDL (triglyceride) synthesis and increase VLDL clearance by increasing lipoprotein lipase activity. *Cholesterol transport inhibitors (ezetimibe):* These drugs can lower LDL cholesterol by 15 to 20% and are frequently added to statin therapy to further boost LDL-lowering efficacy. Vytorin® (simvastatin + ezetimibe in several formulations) is a potent drug

designed to lower LDL cholesterol by 40 to 65%. Omega-3 fatty acids (select OTC brands or Lovaza®): Marine omega-3 fatty acid therapy is prescribed for individuals with high or very high triglycerides. Only at the higher intakes of omega-3 fatty acids (≥2 g/day) are there significant reductions in triglycerides, whereas the lower dosages have other benefits not directly related to triglyceride lowering.

V. (a) high-volume endurance exercise; 48 hours; (b) LDL; HDL; (c) blood triglycerides; (d) 1000; 2000; (e) postprandial lipemia; (f) diminished arterial function; lower HDL cholesterol; exposure of the arterial wall to atherogenic lipoprotein particles; (g) aerobic exercise; 40–70% aerobic capacity; 5 or more days per week; 40–60 minutes; (h) 30,000

VI.

Elevated LDL and/or total cholesterol	≥2000 kcal per week
Low HDL	≥1000 kcal per week
Elevated triglycerides	≥1000 kcal per week
Combined dyslipidemia	≥2000 kcal per week

VII. Clients on statins who are exercising at relatively high intensities or volumes are somewhat more susceptible to exercise-associated muscle aches (myalgia). Although statins are usually well-tolerated, they have occasionally been associated with myopathy and there is a chance that this situation could be exacerbated with exercise. Myopathy is rapidly reversible if diagnosed early by a physician and treated with proper hydration and/or discontinuance of the drug. Although the rare occurrence of statin-induced myopathy should not alarm the ACE-AHFS, it does reinforce the need for the ACE-AHFS to keep reasonably close track of any acute and/or recovery musculoskeletal symptoms through at least the early stages of the exercise program and after statin dose changes.

Show What You Know

Since overall blood lipid improvement is responsive to weekly exercise volumes (total physical-activity energy expenditures) and exercise-generated fat-weight loss, it is imperative that the ACE-AHFS knows how to reliably estimate session, daily, and weekly exercise energy expenditures in kcal. For blood lipid changes or weight loss, the minimal weekly physical-activity goals should be at least 1500 kcal more than entry level physical activity (entry level being evaluated on the first visit). This weekly energy expenditure would be equivalent to about 30,000 or more walking step counts per week beyond the client's weekly baseline step count. Optimal goals are ≥2000 kcal/wk, 200+ minutes per week, and/or ≥70,000 total steps per week. Additionally, although rare, the occurrence of statin-induced myopathy is possible, so Lucy should be encouraged to communicate and record any acute and/or recovery musculoskeletal symptoms through the early stages of the exercise program and after statin dose changes.

Chapter 8

Hypertension

Expand Your Knowledge

I. (1) The incidence of hypertension increases with advancing age, with more than half of Americans over the age of 65 having some form of hypertension. The relation between BP and age is complex. After age 50, SBP steadily increases, whereas DBP plateaus around the sixth decade of life and decreases thereafter. Accordingly, the incidence of isolated systolic hypertension (SBP ≥140) or combined systolic-diastolic hypertension (SBP ≥140 and DBP ≥90) increases with age, while the incidence of isolated diastolic hypertension (DBP ≥90) decreases with age. (2) Cardiac output is the product of heart rate and stroke volume, the volume of blood the heart pumps in one beat. BP is the product of cardiac output and total peripheral resistance. Stroke volume is altered by the amount of blood filling of the heart, the pressure the heart must pump against, and the force of cardiac contractility. Therefore, alterations in these variables resulting in an increase in either cardiac output or total peripheral resistance can cause hypertension. (3) Renin is an enzyme released from the kidneys that activates the hormone angiotensinogen by cleaving off part of the protein to form angiotensin I. Angiotensin I is then converted to angiotensin II via another enzyme called angiotensin converting enzyme (ACE). Angiotensin II is a potent vasoconstrictor that binds to receptors on peripheral blood vessels, causing the vascular smooth muscle in the blood vessels to contract. Angiotensin II also causes the mineral corticoid hormone aldosterone to be released from the adrenal cortex. Aldosterone causes sodium and water to be reabsorbed in the kidneys. Overall, the actions of aldosterone serve to increase blood volume, and consequently, blood pressure. (4) Long-term hypertension can cause the heart muscle to hypertrophy. With hypertension, the heart muscle becomes thicker through concentric hypertrophy and less efficient as a pump. (5) When measuring BP, SBP is the pressure at the point where the first of two or more Korotkoff sounds is heard. DBP is the pressure before the disappearance of the Korotkoff sounds when the heart is relaxed.

II. (1) Weight reduction: 5–20 mmHg/10 kg weight loss; (2) Adopt DASH eating plan: 8–14 mmHg; (3) Dietary sodium reduction: 2–8 mmHg; (4) Physical activity: 4–9 mmHg; (5) Moderation of alcohol consumption: 2–4 mmHg

III. Exercise induces an acute postexercise reduction in both SBP and DBP. This response is known as postexercise hypotension (PEH). The PEH cardiovascular response is characterized by a reduction in peripheral vascular resistance that is not compensated for by an increase in cardiac output, resulting in a decrease in BP. On average, the magnitude of the effect of PEH on BP in hypertensive individuals is approximately 15 and 4 mmHg on SBP and DBP, respectively, and can persist for up to 22 hours following an exercise bout. The PEH response occurs in normotensive and hypertensive men and women of all ages, although the largest reductions in BP occur in hypertensive individuals. There are also significant chronic effects of exercise on BP. Epidemiological studies show that there is an inverse relationship between physical activity and BP. Analysis of studies examining the effects of exercise on BP show that 150 minutes of exercise weekly reduces systolic BP by 2–6 mmHg. Furthermore, physical activity lowers BP in all populations studied, with the greatest reductions in BP occurring in hypertensive individuals.

IV. (1) Diuretics are the most commonly prescribed BP-lowering drugs and are the first-line antihypertensive drugs prescribed for hypertensive patients. This drug class is very effective at lowering BP, especially in cases in which the hypertension is caused by excess extracellular fluid volume. Diuretics initially work to decrease BP by stimulating the excretion of sodium in the proximal tubule of the nephron. To maintain osmotic balance, water follows the sodium, resulting in a loss of extracellular fluid volume. It is hypothesized that the excess sodium contributes to the peripheral blood vessels' rigidity, thus promoting the increase in peripheral vascular resistance. The long-term BP-lowering capabilities of diuretics may be a result of decreasing sodium and indirectly lowering blood vessel rigidity. (2) Beta blockers primarily work to lower BP by antagonizing the beta receptors in the heart and the kidney. In the heart,

normal stimulation of beta receptors by epinephrine increases heart rate and increases calcium entry into the myocardial cells, thereby increasing contractility. Stimulation of these receptors causes an increase in cardiac output. Blocking the beta receptors therefore decreases heart rate and contractility, collectively causing a decreased cardiac output. Initially, the antihypertensive effect of beta blockers is due to this decrease in cardiac output. Beta blockers also inhibit renin release as a result of sympathetic nerve stimulation to the kidney. Blocking the beta receptors in the kidney results in a passive vasodilation of the peripheral vasculature, thereby lowering peripheral vascular resistance. (3) Angiotensin converting enzyme (ACE) inhibitors block the conversion of angiotensin I to angiotensin II in the RAAS, which results in an inhibition of peripheral vasoconstriction mediated by angiotensin II in the vasculature. It also results in an inhibition of aldosterone release from the adrenal cortex, thus preventing sodium and water reabsorption in the kidney. One of the advantages of ACE inhibitors is that they cause vasodilation of the peripheral vasculature without inducing a compensatory increase in sympathetic nerve activity. (4) Angiotensin receptor blockers (ARBs) are similar to ACE inhibitors in the way that they lower BP. However, instead of inhibiting the production of angiotensin II, they block the receptor on which angiotensin II acts. ARBs cause a decrease in peripheral vasoconstriction, resulting in a decrease in peripheral vascular resistance. Furthermore, ARBs also inhibit the release of aldosterone from the adrenal cortex, which ultimately inhibits sodium and water reabsorption in the kidney. (5) Aldosterone-receptor antagonists inhibit the effect of aldosterone on the kidney. Thus, sodium and water are not reabsorbed and plasma volume is decreased. (6) Alpha blockers work by inhibiting the alpha 1 receptors in the peripheral blood vessels, leading to a reduction in vasoconstriction and reduced peripheral vascular resistance. However, when the alpha 1 receptors are blocked, there is a compensatory increase in heart rate in an attempt to increase BP to achieve homeostatic balance. (7) Calcium (Ca++) channel blockers prevent calcium from entering the cardiac and vascular smooth muscle cells. This in turn causes a decrease in cardiac contractility, a decrease in conduction of the electrical signal that controls heart rate, and a decrease in peripheral blood vessel vasoconstriction. The BP-lowering action of Ca++ channel blockers is therefore twofold, in that they reduce both cardiac output and peripheral vascular resistance. (8) Central acting alpha 2 blockers work in the BP control centers in the brain to reset and lower the BP set point, which reduces sympathetic activity to the heart and increases parasympathetic activity, resulting in a slowing of the heart rate. In addition, the reduction in sympathetic activity to the peripheral blood vessels and kidneys decreases vasoconstriction, which decreases peripheral vascular resistance and decreases renin release from the kidney. (9) Peripheral vasodilators cause vasodilation and reduce BP by relaxing the vascular smooth muscle in the peripheral blood vessels. Typically, peripheral vasodilators are only used in combination with other antihypertensive drugs in cases of resistant hypertension or a hypertensive crisis.

V. (a) lower; (b) hypertensive; (c) a decrease in peripheral vascular resistance; (d) decrease; (e) norepinephrine; (f) reduced responsiveness to norepinephrine; decreased endothelin 1; increased nitric oxide; structural adaptations; (g) diminished; (h) cardiovascular pathology; (i) diuretics

VI. (1) On most, preferably all, days of the week; (2) Moderate (40–60% $\dot{V}O_2$max or 12–13 RPE); (3) 30–60 minutes of continuous or accumulated physical activity; (4) Rhythmic aerobic exercise that targets large muscle groups; should be individualized

VII. Resistance training has a positive effect on insulin sensitivity. There is a significant link between decreased insulin sensitivity and hypertension. Because consistent and long-term resistance training increases insulin sensitivity, this may be one of the mechanisms mediating the reduction in BP. Resistance training also attenuates the rate-pressure product when lifting any given load, which decreases the demand on the heart when performing activities of daily living. Because circuit training uses lighter weights with limited rest periods between exercises, thereby introducing an aerobic component, it is the type of resistance training recommended for hypertensive clients. Mind-body exercises such as yoga and tai chi can provide a beneficial reduction in blood pressure attributable to both physical activity and relaxation. The combined effects on blood pressure of physical activity and relaxation, as practiced through mind-body exercise, appear to be synergistic, meaning that the combined effect is greater than the individual BP-lowering capabilities of either physical activity or relaxation alone. Mind-body exercise practiced regularly also improves balance and upper- and lower-body muscular strength and endurance. Further, these mind-body exercises also improve proprioceptive awareness.

Show What You Know

Initial exercise recommendations for Jerry follow ACSM's FITT principle:

Frequency: On most, preferably all, days of the week

Intensity: Moderate (40–60% $\dot{V}O_2$max or 12–13 RPE)

Time: 30–60 minutes of continuous or accumulated physical activity

Type: Rhythmic aerobic exercise that targets large muscle groups; should be individualized

Atenolol is a beta blocker that blunts the normal elevation in heart rate that is observed during exercise. Therefore, gauging exercise intensity via target heart rate when working with Jerry is not appropriate. Instead, ratings of perceived exertion (RPE) of "somewhat hard," which equates to a 13 on the Borg scale (6 to 20 scale), should be used to evaluate exercise intensity. In addition to the heart-rate response, there are other precautions that an ACE-AHFS should be aware of with this class of drugs. First, beta blockers can sometimes mask the symptoms of hypoglycemia (low blood sugar). Because exercise also decreases blood sugar, significant hypoglycemia during exercise can sometimes occur in clients taking beta blockers. Second, some clients taking beta blockers may complain of exercise intolerance due to the blunted heart-rate response. If this occurs, it is important that Jerry see his healthcare provider to adjust the medication. He must not abruptly stop taking his medication, as doing so can result in rebound hypertension. Lastly, beta blockers can cause fatigue, sedation, depression, and sexual dysfunction. If Jerry complains of these symptoms, it is important that he sees the appropriate healthcare provider.

Chapter 9

Asthma

Expand Your Knowledge

I. (1) The two most important triggers are allergens and viral respiratory infections. Exposure to house-dust mites and cockroaches in early life increases the risk of asthma in susceptible children. Exposure to dog and cat dander may also increase the risk of asthma. Likewise, exposure to respiratory syncytial virus (RSV) or parainfluenza virus as an infant seems to increase the risk of asthma in later childhood, with nearly 40% of these infants wheezing or acquiring asthma in later childhood. (2) According to the "hygiene hypothesis," exposure to various viral infections, including RSV, in early life decreases the risk of developing asthma by promoting the development of a child's immune system along a "non-allergic" pathway. (3) Use of accessory muscles to breathe; the appearance of hunched shoulders and/or chest deformity; sounds of wheezing during normal breathing or prolonged forced exhalation; increased nasal secretion, mucosal swelling, and/or nasal polyp; and eczema and other signs of an allergic skin condition. (4) Spirometry measures lung function by assessing the amount and/or speed of air that can be maximally inhaled and exhaled. In spirometric testing, the patient takes a deep breath and blows into a mouthpiece attached to the spirometer. The patient is then instructed to exhale as hard and fast as possible until the lungs feel completely empty. A computerized sensor in the spirometer calculates and graphs the results. The patient is then given a short-acting bronchodilator or nebulizer and the sequence is repeated. A decrease in airflow in people with asthma usually can be partially reversed with short-acting bronchodilators or nebulizers. Spirometry is performed at the time of initial assessment; after treatment is initiated and symptoms and peak expiratory flow (PEF) have stabilized; during a period of poorly controlled symptoms; and at least every one to two years to assess maintenance of airway function.

II. (1) Keep furred or feathered pets out of the home. If you can't keep the pet outdoors, then keep the pet out of the bedroom and other sleeping areas at all times and keep the door closed; remove carpets and furniture covered with cloth from the home; and if that is not possible, keep the pet away from fabric-covered furniture and carpets.

(2) Encase the mattress in a special dust-proof cover; encase pillows in a special dust-proof cover or wash the pillows each week in hot water; wash the sheets and blankets on the bed each week in hot water; reduce indoor humidity to below 60%; try not to sleep or lie on cloth-covered cushions; remove carpets from the bedroom and those laid on concrete; keep stuffed toys out of the bed or wash the toys weekly in hot water or cooler water with detergent and bleach. (3) Keep food and garbage in closed containers; never leave food out; use poison baits, powders, gels, paste, or traps; if a spray is used to kill roaches, stay out of the room until the odor goes away. (4) Fix leaky faucets, pipes, or other sources of water that have mold around them; clean moldy surfaces with a cleaner that has bleach in it. (5) Try to keep windows closed; stay indoors with windows closed from late morning to afternoon, if possible; ask the doctor whether to take or increase anti-inflammatory medicine before allergy season starts. (6) If you smoke, ask your doctor for ways to help you quit; ask family members to quit smoking, too; do not allow smoking in your home or car. (7) If possible, do not use a wood-burning stove, kerosene heater, or fireplace; try to stay away from strong odors and sprays, such as perfume, talcum powder, hair spray, and paints. (8) Try to get someone else to vacuum for you once or twice a week, if possible; stay out of rooms while they are being vacuumed and for a short while afterward; if you vacuum, use a dust mask, a double-layered or microfilter vacuum cleaner bag, or a vacuum cleaner with a HEPA filter.

III. *Green zone* (≥80% of personal best) signals good control. No asthma symptoms are present. The individual should take medications as usual. *Yellow zone* (50–80% of personal best) signals caution. If measurements remain in this zone, the individual should take an inhaled short-acting beta agonist. If peak flows continue to be in the yellow zone, this may signal that asthma is not under good control. The client should consult with his or her physician to change or increase daily medications. *Red zone* (<50% of personal best) signals a medical alert. The individual must take a short-acting beta-agonist immediately. The ACE-AHFS should call the client's physician or the emergency room and ask what to do, or take the client directly to the emergency room. If the client is alone, he or she should call 911.

IV. Long-term-control medications prevent symptoms, usually by reducing inflammation. These medications must be taken daily and do not typically provide quick relief. Quick-relief medications are short-acting beta-agonists that act to relax muscles around the airway and provide rapid improvement of symptoms. Quick-relief medications should only be used when symptoms occur. The need for these medications on a regular basis may indicate insufficiently controlled asthma and the need to start or increase long-term-control medications.

V. (1) What are your triggers? (2) What medications do you take (including those prescribed by a physician and any over-the-counter or alternative therapies)? (3) When was your last asthma exacerbation? (4) When was the last time you saw your physician? (5) Is your physician aware of everything that you have disclosed to me?

VI. (1) Reduce exercise intensity so that the client can easily administer rescue medication according to his or her asthma action plan. Do not encourage the client to "push through" an attack or stop the exercise abruptly. (2) Remove the client from any environmental allergens or irritants, such as cold or polluted air, that may be contributing to the symptoms. (3) Provide calm support and coach the client to use diaphragmatic breathing, taking deep breaths in through the nose and extending through the abdomen, and out through the mouth and drawing in the abdomen. (4) If symptoms persist, discontinue exercise and seek immediate medical attention. (5) Follow the gym or business protocol to document the incident and the actions taken.

VII. (a) 7; (b) 3; (c) 6; (d) 1; (e) 8; (f) 4; (g) 2; (h) 5; (i) 9

VIII. (1) Avoid asthma triggers during exercise. (2) Always have rescue medication nearby for use in the event of an attack. (3) Establish a flexible program that can accommodate fluctuations in exercise capacity due to asthma symptoms. (4) Utilize an extended warm-up and cool-down. (5) Emphasize hydration before, during, and after exercise. (6) Have the client practice diaphragmatic breathing. (7) Determine exercise intensity according to the client's state of deconditioning, psychological preparedness for exercise, and asthma severity. (8) Incorporate intervals for high-intensity training. (9) Closely monitor the client for early signs of an asthma attack and respond immediately. Get medical help if symptoms do not subside. (10) Use ratings of perceived exertion and the dyspnea scale to communicate with the client regarding symptoms. (11) Choose exercise testing methods that accommodate a warm-up period.

Show What You Know

Encourage Sarah to follow her asthma action plan if she has one. Otherwise, the best way to control acute symptoms is usually to markedly decrease or discontinue activity and use a rescue inhaler to open the airways. Sarah should seek immediate medical assistance if symptoms persist or worsen. Since her symptoms were most likely triggered by a combination of exercise and an environmental contaminant (pollen), and since she had never experienced an exercise-induced bronchospasm (EIB) prior to this workout, Sarah should be referred to her physician following the exercise bout. The physician can then arrange an exercise challenge in which Sarah engages in sufficiently strenuous activity to increase heart rate to 80% of MHR for four to six minutes. A 15% decrease in PEF or FEV1 confirms a diagnosis of EIB.

Chapter 10

Overweight and Obesity

Expand Your Knowledge

I. (1) The primary reason for overweight and obesity is a positive energy balance, wherein intake (via calories consumed from food and beverages) is greater than output (energy expenditure from resting metabolism, physical activity, and exercise). Energy balance occurs when energy intake equals energy output, while a negative energy balance leads to weight loss. (2) Fat found in the trunk area around the internal organs of the abdomen (often observed in men) is referred to as android or visceral fat. Excess visceral fat is correlated with hypertension, diabetes, high blood triglycerides and coronary heart disease. (3) Leptin, which resides in all fat cells, is a hormone that communicates directly with the hypothalamus, providing information about how much energy is currently stored in the body's fat cells. When fat cells decrease in size, leptin decreases, sending a message to the hypothalamus to direct the body to eat more. Similarly, when fat cells increase in size, leptin increases and the message sent to the hypothalamus is to instruct the body to eat less. However, it appears that the primary biological role of leptin is to facilitate energy intake when energy storage is low, as opposed to slowing down overconsumption when energy storage is high. Another specialized hormone secreted by fat is adiponectin, which helps insulin by sending blood glucose into the body's cells for storage or use as fuel, thus increasing the cells' insulin sensitivity or glucose metabolism. It also helps decrease blood levels of triglycerides by working with insulin to stimulate fat breakdown. In summary, leptin stimulates the appetite, whereas adiponectin aids in the breakdown of fat. (4) Cytokines, which are hormone-like proteins, function largely as inflammatory proteins, reacting to areas of infection or injury in the body. However, persons with excess fat appear to have an overreaction in terms of the release of these inflammatory proteins. This may be caused by the low oxygen content in the clusters of adipocytes, which are somewhat distant from the tissues' vascular supply. Both obesity and diabetes are associated with chronic low-grade inflammation. (5) Ghrelin, secreted by the stomach, plays a chief role in appetite regulation. It is recognized as the "hunger hormone." High levels of ghrelin during a fasted state promote increased food intake, while lower levels of ghrelin are observed after eating a meal. When the body feels that it has eaten enough, the hormone peptide YY is released from the intestines. It is particularly stimulated by lipids and carbohydrates. This gut hormone is thought to work with the central nervous system to regulate the cessation of appetite. Thus, when released, it provides a feeling of satiety. (6) Research suggests that lean persons have significantly more total-body ambulatory movement, such as standing and walking, throughout their day than overweight persons. Therefore, encouraging NEAT may be a very important way to help clients achieve their weight-loss and body-composition goals.

II. Dietary intervention, behavioral therapy, and physical activity.

III. (1) Fruits, which can be canned (in juice or water), fresh, frozen, or dried; (2) Vegetables, which can be canned (without salt), fresh, frozen, or dried; (3) Fat-free and low-fat milk and milk products such as low-fat yogurt and cheese; (4) Lean meat, poultry, fish, lentils, and beans; (5) Whole-grain foods such as oatmeal, brown rice, bagels, bread, pasta, cereal, tortillas, and crackers; (6) Canola or olive oils and soft margarines made from these oils in small amounts, because they are high in calories; (7) Unsalted nuts, like walnuts and almonds, in small amounts due their high caloric value

IV. (1) Properly assess the client's readiness to change. (2) Teach accurate self-monitoring of food consumption. (3) Set realistic goals. (4) Incorporate sound dietary change. (5) Increase physical activity. (6) Utilize stimulus control. (7) Utilize cognitive restructuring. (8) Utilize relapse management. (9) Establish ongoing support.

V. (1) Frequent self-monitoring of body weight and food intake; (2) Eating a diet low in fat and higher in carbohydrate; (3) Eating breakfast and regular meals; (4) Limiting fast food; (5) Accepting realistic weight goals; (6) Performing high levels of physical activity (≥1 hour/day); (7) Recognizing that weight control is an ongoing process and commitment

VI. The accumulated time approach addresses the fact that energy expenditure is actually a cumulative phenomenon, including both low-intensity activities of daily life, such as walking and recreational dancing, and more vigorous exercise like swimming, elliptical training, and cycling. When pursuing weight-management goals, the evidence suggests that overweight and obese persons should gradually progress to 60 minutes per day of accumulated exercise.

VII. RMR accounts for 60 to 75% of all calorie-burning processes. Although muscle is the largest tissue in the body, its estimated RMR is below what has been publicized in the consumer media. In fact, scientific estimation of the metabolic rate of muscle is about 10 to 15 kcal/kg per day, which is approximately 4.5 to 7.0 kcal/lb per day. Although not nearly as much as is promoted, this small effect may lead to a cumulative calorie deficit of up to 350 calories in a week. Therefore, although the magnitude of this change may seem small, the overall contribution of resistance training to weight loss is quite meaningful to weight-loss goals.

VIII. Sibutramine prevents the removal of norepinephrine and serotonin in the brain, thus prolonging some of their appetite-suppressing effects. The research on sibutramine suggests that it is relatively safe, minimally elevating heart rate (4 bpm) and blood pressure (2 to 4 mmHg for both systolic and diastolic blood pressure). A minor increase of high-density lipoproteins (HDL) and a mild reduction in triglycerides have also been observed. Orlistat's primary function is preventing the intestinal absorption of fats from the diet, thereby reducing the caloric impact of food consumed. It is intended for use in combination with a physician-supervised reduced-calorie diet. Orlistat is successful at blocking absorption of approximately 30% of dietary fat. Researchers note that orlistat has been shown to have considerable gastrointestinal side effects, including abdominal pain, diarrhea, flatulence, bloating, and upset stomach.

IX. (1) Establish a long-term reduction in body weight of at least 5 to 10%. (2) The primary mode of exercise should be large-muscle-group aerobic activities. (3) A combination of weightbearing and nonweightbearing activities is encouraged. (4) The initial emphasis of the exercise training should be on duration and frequency (keeping intensity moderate and progressing gradually). (5) Frequency of training should be five to seven days per week. (6) Accumulate 200 to 300 minutes of aerobic activity per week (which is equivalent to ≥2000 kilocalories of exercise per week); this can be accomplished via exercise bouts lasting as little as 10 minutes. (7) Include a reduction in dietary fat intake to <30% of total energy intake. (8) Emphasize fruits, vegetables, whole grains, and lean sources of protein. (9) Create a negative energy balance of 500 to 1000 kilocalories per day [which is equivalent to a weekly weight loss of 1 to 2 pounds (0.5 to 1.0 kg)]. (10) Include the use of behavior-management techniques (including relapse prevention).

X. (1) Aquatic exercise programs provide total-body exercise with little to no weightbearing due to the buoyancy of water. Buoyancy is a benefit for overweight and obese people who may have joint problems (such as arthritis of the knee, hip, or ankle, or structural problems of these three joints). (2) Recumbent stationary cycling is a great option for obese individuals, as compared to stationary or road cycling, due to the balance advantages, a safe indoor environment, and no impact on the joints. (3) Walking is considered a very good initial exercise because it requires no extra skill. When beginning a walking or weightbearing exercise regimen with a client, make sure the person has quality fitness shoes with good, shock-absorbing qualities. (4) Cross-training helps to thwart the occurrence of musculoskeletal system stress, and aids in the prevention of muscle soreness and injuries. Therefore, theoretically, a person will be able to safely do more work more frequently, which equates to higher total energy expenditure and fat utilization. (5) Circuit training research has shown meaningful changes in body composition. Thus, one of the noteworthy benefits of this type of resistance exercise, as it relates to body composition in overweight populations, is the positive impact of maintaining or increasing fat-free body mass, while encouraging the loss of fat weight via a progressive-overload resistance-training program.

Show What You Know

Since Tessa has achieved a base level of cardiorespiratory conditioning, as evidenced by her ability to walk continuously for 45 minutes, she should consider including some cardiorespiratory workouts that are of higher intensity for a shorter period of time. This objective may best be realized with interval training. To avoid physiological and orthopedic stress and injury, it would be prudent for Sarah to complete only one higher-intensity workout per week. She should also incorporate cross-training so that she avoid becoming overly fatigued from overuse of the same muscles in the same movement patterns. This will help prevent musculoskeletal system stress and aid in the prevention of muscle soreness and injuries. Lastly, Sarah should be encouraged to vary her workouts regularly to provide a new stimulus to her cardiorespiratory system in an effort to avoid the consequences of overuse exercise fatigue.

Chapter 11

The Metabolic Syndrome

Expand Your Knowledge

I. (a) 4%; (b) reduced; (c) 2 mg/L; (d) 30 kg/m²; (e) reduction of abdominal adiposity; (f) polyunsaturated; monounsaturated; saturated; (g) Bariatric; (h) fivefold; one-and-a-half- to threefold

II. (1) Abdominal obesity indicated by a waist circumference ≥40 inches (102 cm) in men and ≥35 inches (88 cm) in women; (2) Levels of triglyceride ≥150 mg/dL (1.7 mmol/L); (3) HDL levels <40 and 50 mg/dL (1.0 and 1.3 mmol/L) in men and women, respectively; (4) Blood pressure levels ≥130/85 mmHg; (5) Fasting glucose levels ≥110 mg/dL (6.1 mmol/L)

III.

Nutrient	Recommended Intake
Saturated fat	<7% of total calories
Polyunsaturated fat	Up to 10% of total calories
Monounsaturated fat	Up to 20% of total calories
Total fat	25–35% of total calories
Carbohydrate	50–60% of total calories
Fiber	20–30 grams/day
Protein	Approximately 15% of total calories
Cholesterol	<200 mg/day
Total calories	Balance energy intake and expenditure to maintain a desirable body weight/prevent weight gain

IV. (1) Elevated blood pressure; (2) Insulin resistance; (3) Impaired glucose metabolism; (4) Dyslipidemia

V. The transition from the metabolic syndrome to overt type 2 diabetes stems from insulin resistance and a decline of pancreatic beta-cell function. Insulin resistance in muscle tissue results in decreased glucose uptake and impaired glycogen synthesis. In the liver, insulin resistance results in failure of insulin to suppress hepatic glucose production. Despite these anomalies, individuals are normoglycemic in the early stages of the disease due to a marked increase in pancreatic beta-cell insulin secretion. As the disease progresses, glucotoxicity and lipotoxicity cause beta-cell function to decline, leading to apoptosis of pancreatic islet cells. At this point, the lower level of insulin secretion can no longer compensate for the effects of insulin resistance, and serum glucose levels reach the threshold for type 2 diabetes.

VI. With an increasingly hypokinetic lifestyle, skeletal muscle down-regulates its capacity to convert nutritional substrates to ATP. Inactive skeletal muscle's impaired ability to oxidize glucose and fatty acids is mediated by several mechanisms, including decreased mitochondrial concentration; a reduced ability to remove glucose from blood due to fewer capillaries and diminished glucose transporter; and an attenuated capacity to hydrolyze blood triglycerides to free fatty acids, secondary to decreased lipoprotein lipase activity. Collectively, these metabolic perturbations serve to reduce the capacity to burn fuel, resulting in hyperinsulinemia, hypertriglyceridemia, and ultimately increased cardiovascular risk.

VII. The metabolic syndrome may also serve as a respiratory stress, especially in individuals with concomitant abdominal obesity. As adiposity develops, breathing requires increased effort, owing to the expanded mass of the chest wall, elevation of the diaphragm, and compression of a protruding abdomen. Dyspnea on exertion may result because the depth of breathing is compromised, and the only way increased ventilation can occur is by increasing the individual's breathing frequency. Varied indices of breathing economy may be adversely affected, such as the minute ventilation/oxygen consumption slope or the minute ventilation/carbon dioxide production slope, as well as associated responses, including hypoxia, hypercapnia, respiratory acidosis, somnolence, and pulmonary hypertension.

VIII. (1) Five days per week or daily. More frequent structured exercise bouts are desirable, but care should be taken to initially establish a regular exercise habit (3–5 days/week); 3–4 sessions per week are required to elicit beneficial metabolic effects, whereas 4–5 sessions per week (or more) may be needed to reduce body weight and fat stores.

(2) 30/45–75% $\dot{V}O_2$ reserve. To avoid musculoskeletal injuries and maximize compliance, start at a light-to-moderate intensity and gradually progress over the course of several weeks or months to vigorous exercise (>60% $\dot{V}O_2$ reserve or heart-rate reserve) (if desired by the client). Initially emphasize increasing duration rather than intensity, with the goal of optimizing caloric expenditure. (3) 30 to 90 minutes/day, using a gradual progression. Multiple shorter periods of exercise (10–15 minute exercise bouts) accumulated throughout the day may elicit similar (or even greater) reductions in body weight and fat stores as a single long bout of the same total duration. (4) Low-impact activities (walking, low-impact aerobics, cycling). These activities are convenient, accessible, and perceived as enjoyable by the client, and should be supplemented by adjunctive resistance training to assist in the maintenance of basal metabolic rate as well an increase in daily lifestyle activities (walking breaks at work, gardening, household work).

Show What You Know

Jason meets all five of the criteria for the metabolic syndrome: abdominal obesity indicated by a waist circumference ≥40 inches (102 cm); levels of triglyceride ≥150 mg/dL; HDL levels <40 mg/dL; blood pressure levels ≥130/85 mmHg; and fasting glucose levels ≥110 mg/dL. Since the metabolic syndrome is defined by having three of the five criteria, Jason appears to have the condition. A program of regular physical activity would help Jason decrease his waist circumference, blood pressure, fasting blood glucose, and triglycerides, as well as increase his HDL cholesterol. These improvements could be enough to move Jason out of the metabolic syndrome classification and decrease his risk of developing type 2 diabetes and cardiovascular disease.

Chapter 12

Diabetes Mellitus

Expand Your Knowledge

I. (a) T1DM; (b) T2DM; (c) T1DM; (d) T1DM & T2DM; (e) T2DM; (f) T2DM; (g) T2DM; (h) T1DM; (i) T1DM & T2DM; (j) T1DM

II. Fasting blood glucose >126 mg/dL; diabetes symptoms, plus casual plasma glucose >200 mg/dL; and two-hour glucose >200 mg/dL during an oral glucose tolerance test using a 75-gram glucose load

III. Macrovascular disease is associated with accelerated coronary heart disease and an accelerated atherogenic process in other large vessels, including those in the lower extremities (peripheral vasculature) and in the brain (cerebral vasculature). Lower-extremity complications usually limit the weightbearing tolerance of afflicted individuals and contribute to a greater risk of non-traumatic amputations. Microvascular complications and nerve diseases are common outcomes of long-standing diabetes. The three different types of microvascular and neural complications are retinopathy (eye disease), nephropathy (kidney disease), and neuropathy (nerve disease). These complications of diabetes are the leading cause of new blindness, end-stage renal disease and kidney failure in adults, and nervous system damage leading to numerous amputations, respectively. Moreover, these complications affect work performance and tolerance, as well as the mode and intensity of work performed.

IV. Exercise can accelerate the mobilization of insulin if the injection site is in the exercising muscle. Also, insulin dosage (pump or injection) can be reduced prior to exercise to avoid hypoglycemia. There are also two injectable medications that aid glucose management and are used by individuals with T1DM and/or T2DM: Byetta® (exenatide or extendin-4) and Symlin® (pramlintide). The main exercise-related concern associated with these medications is that they both delay the emptying of food from the gut after a meal and could slow the release of ingested carbohydrates taken to prevent or treat low blood glucose levels during a bout of exercise. Consequently, to err on the side of safety, neither Byetta nor Symlin should be injected within two hours prior to scheduled physical activity. Four major groups of oral agents are used to control glucose: beta-cell stimulants for insulin release, drugs to improve insulin sensitivity, drugs to abate intestinal absorption of carbohydrates, and drugs to extend the action of insulin. Beta-cell stimulants are taken at mealtime to stimulate insulin release and manage postprandial glycemia. Because of insulin stimulation, these oral agents can lead to hypoglycemia with or without exercise. The prolonged length of action in these oral agents increases the risk for low blood glucose and requires more frequent monitoring during exercise. Drugs to improve insulin sensitivity at muscle and adipose tissue have little effect on exercise responses. Insulin sensitizers mainly improve the action of insulin at rest, not during exercise, so the risk of them causing exercise-associated hypoglycemia is very low. Drugs to abate intestinal absorption of carbohydrates decrease the carbohydrate absorption rate and slow the increase in postprandial blood glucose level. These medications do not directly affect exercise, but can delay effective treatment of hypoglycemia during activities by slowing the absorption of carbohydrates ingested to treat this condition. Drugs to extend the action of insulin may not increase the risk of exercise-induced hypoglycemia in individuals with type 2 diabetes who are already being treated with metformin.

V. A1C% (glycosylated hemoglobin): <7%, checked at least twice a year; Blood pressure: <130/80 mmHg, checked at every doctor's visit; Cholesterol: LDL <100 mg/dL, checked at least once a year

VI. In type 1 diabetics, aerobic capacity has been suggested to be lower than that of non-diabetic, healthy individuals. Nonetheless, physical training through aerobic workouts and/or resistance training is commonly recommended for individuals with T1DM who are without complications. Such individuals tend to exhibit chronic exercise benefits similar to those observed in non-diabetics. However, regular exercise is not effective for improving long-term blood glucose control of T1DM and should not be the sole means of controlling blood glucose. Although regular exercise improves metabolism in individuals with T1DM, it does not facilitate the desired level of metabolic control. Cardiovascular training in T1DM favorably alters common CVD risk factors, including blood lipids, blood pressure, insulin resistance, and glucose control. Therefore, improving aerobic fitness and muscular fitness in individuals with T1DM is central to improving cardiovascular health and lessening CVD risk. In type 2 diabetics, regular exercise improves insulin signaling and insulin resistance. The more that individuals with T2DM engage in physical activity throughout each week, the lower the insulin levels and the greater the insulin sensitivity or the lower the insulin resistance. Along with nutrition therapy, regular exercise promotes improved cardiovascular and metabolic functions, reduced risk of cardiac morbidity and mortality and favorable changes in lipids and lipoproteins, blood pressure, body weight, fat-free mass, fat mass, body-fat distribution and morphology, insulin sensitivity and insulin concentrations, and glucose metabolism. Also, strength training has been shown to improve muscle function and quality, while increasing insulin sensitivity in individuals with T2DM. Most importantly, the glucose metabolic defects found in previously sedentary individuals with T2DM are reversed with exercise, while both insulin signaling and exercise signaling of glucose transport are markedly improved with moderate-intensity exercise performed consistently over time. Consequently, regular exercise training improves long-term glucose control in T2DM, primarily through improved insulin signaling and insulin sensitivity. These combined physiological changes can actually lower daily medication dose for individuals with T2DM. In general, exercise training appears to reverse inflammatory markers and postreceptor insulin signaling defects, and encourage intramuscular and abdominal fat use, while simultaneously lowering the metabolic and atherosclerotic risks associated with T2DM.

VII. Exercise stress tests are advisable for all persons with diabetes who are older than 35 years of age, and for people who are older than 25 years of age who have had T1DM for more than 15 years or T2DM for more than 10 years. Also, a stress test may be needed to assess cardiorespiratory integrity if a client is to embark on moderate-to-high intensity physical activity and is at high risk for underlying cardiovascular disease.

VIII. The FITT program differs for individuals with T1DM and T2DM, in that a T1DM program can emphasize exercise at a moderate-to-high intensity for shorter durations, while a program for individuals with T2DM should emphasize caloric expenditure where lower-intensity and longer-duration exercise is strongly encouraged. In individuals with T1DM without complications, exercise recommendations are closely aligned with apparently healthy persons, while recommendations for those withT2DM are more closely aligned with obesity and hypertension guidelines due to the high prevalence of these comorbidities in T2DM. Also, individuals with T2DM are encouraged to engage in at least 150 minutes of moderate-intensity exercise each week (or 90 minutes of vigorous exercise each week), primarily focusing on caloric expenditure and weight-management issues. For long-term weight-loss maintenance, larger volumes of exercise (seven hours/week of moderate or vigorous activity, with an expenditure of more than 2000 kcal/week) are recommended for clients with T2DM.

IX. (1) Clients should perform SBGM before and after each physical-activity session. SBGM is excellent cognitive training for diabetics to understand individual glucose response to physical activity. It is important to ensure that blood glucose is in relatively good control before engaging in purposeful exercise. (2) If blood glucose is >250 mg/dL with ketones, physical activity should be postponed. (3) If blood glucose is <100 mg/dL, the client should eat a snack consisting of carbohydrates and recheck blood glucose before exercising. (4) If blood glucose is between 100 and 250 mg/dL, physical activity can be safely performed.

X. (1) An inability to accurately palpate and obtain a heart rate; (2) A loss of sensation in the feet or toes during weightbearing activities; (3) Increasing pain in the legs during weightbearing activities; (4) Difficulty reading the RPE chart; (5) Unusual forgetfulness or memory problems; (6) Persistent fatigue

XI. (1) Hypoinsulinemia, or insulin deficiency, results in elevated blood glucose and ketone bodies before exercise. Insulin-deficient diabetics rely heavily upon free fatty acids (FFA) as a primary energy source, which leads to elevated ketones in the blood and urine. As work increases, there is an increase in metabolic functions to provide adequate fuel for the body. A person with inadequate insulin is not able to adequately regulate blood glucose levels, and therefore experiences an increase in blood glucose, along with an increase in FFA use and ketone production. Exercise seems to worsen hyperglycemia in an insulin-deficient state because insulin action does not promote normal metabolic functions. (2) Hyperinsulinemia, or high insulin levels, usually occurs when exogenous insulin is accelerated by increased muscle contraction and blood flow. This situation can cause exercise-induced hypoglycemia. Insulin injection into non-active muscle is recommended on exercising days, although the strict use of non-active muscle as an injection site may not prevent hypoglycemia during exercise in those with T1DM. Elevated insulin levels suppress hepatic glucose production, which causes an imbalance between the rate of peripheral glucose use and production, and results in the lowering of blood glucose. Although a decrease in blood glucose is a beneficial short-term effect of exercise, prolonged exercise can bring about hypoglycemia.

XII. (1) Profuse sweating; (2) Clamminess and pallor; (3) Shakiness; (4) Difficulty answering specific questions; (5) Slurred speech; (6) Exhaustion; (7) Lightheadedness or fainting

XIII. For those who use insulin injections, the insulin injection should occur at least one hour before exercising, and preferably in a non-exercising area.

XIV. (1) Diabetics with proliferative retinopathy who engage in low-intensity exercise can significantly improve cardiovascular function. However, systolic blood pressure should be monitored during each exercise session and limited to increasing 20 to 30 mmHg above resting. Clients with retinopathy may exercise safely when they are properly supervised. Clients with retinopathy should not engage in activities that require them to raise their arms over their heads, such as strength training. These activities may cause systolic blood pressure to rise dramatically. Under such circumstances, increased blood pressure may increase the likelihood of retinal hemorrhaging when proliferative retinopathy is present. (2) Increased blood pressure is a common precursor to worsening of this microvascular disease.

It is prudent to avoid activities that cause systolic blood pressure to rise to 180 to 200 mmHg, as systemic pressure increases could potentially exacerbate the progression of this disease. Persons with progressive nephropathy or end-stage renal disease may benefit from lower-intensity physical activities. Most clients with nephropathy should be referred to a clinical setting where their fragile metabolic condition may be carefully monitored. (3) The two main nerve diseases related to diabetes are autonomic neuropathy (AN), and peripheral neuropathy (PN). When neuropathy affects the autonomic nerves to the heart, it is called cardiac autonomic neuropathy (CAN). The heart rate is altered. The maximal heart rate is blunted, while resting heart rate (HRrest) increases (e.g., HRrest >100 bpm). CAN can cause hypertension and hypotension and increases the risk for exercise-induced hypotension after strenuous activity. Persons with AN have impaired sweating and thermoregulatory abilities and impaired hypoglycemia awareness. Persons with CAN exhibit a lower fitness level and fatigue at relatively low workloads due to the disruption in nerve innervation to the heart. Consequently, physical activity for these persons should focus on low-level daily activities, where mild changes in heart rate and blood pressure can be accommodated. Before beginning any exercise program for persons with AN or CAN, the ACE-AHFS should gain physician approval and proceed cautiously. Peripheral nerve disease affects the extremities, especially the lower legs and feet. Repeated weightbearing activities on insensitive feet can lead to chronic irritation, open sores, and musculoskeletal injuries, especially fractures. Persons with PN are susceptible to overstretching due to loss of sensation, as well as infection, particularly when daily hygiene is lacking.

Proper footwear for any weightbearing activity is important to prevent undetectable sores, which may turn into infections. However, people with PN should also participate in non-weightbearing activities. Additionally, activities requiring a full range of joint motion are highly effective in reducing stiffness due to muscle contractures. Some mind/body exercise activities (e.g., yoga, Pilates, and tai chi) may be prudent for the client who has PN.

Show What You Know

Marcia should ingest a simple sugar snack (e.g., candy) or drink (e.g., orange juice) that contains about 20 to 30 grams of carbohydrate. After five minutes, her blood glucose should be checked to determine whether more carbohydrates are needed. This cycle should be repeated until her blood glucose returns close to 100 mg/dL before engaging in exercise. Following an insulin reaction, Marcia may not feel comfortable exercising. If this is the case, the exercise session should be terminated.

Chapter 13

Posture and Movement

Expand Your Knowledge

I. (1) A tight muscle experiences a lowered activation threshold, which can be described as becoming overactive or hypertonic. Hypertonic muscles decrease neural activity to the lengthened antagonists via reciprocal inhibition and contribute to a progressive weakening (latency) of that muscle. (2) A muscle that assists an agonist in causing a desired action is a synergist. A synergist may act as a joint stabilizer, neutralize rotation, or be activated when the external resistance increases, or when an agonist becomes fatigued or inhibited. (3) Thoracic kyphosis represents excessive posterior curvature of the thoracic spine. The upper thoracic spine normally has a rounded contour, but this curve can be accentuated secondarily due to factors such as osteoporosis. (4) Side dominance can result in postural asymmetry due to a general over-reliance on the dominant side. A right-handed individual may exhibit a right shoulder that is lower than the left given the frequency of reaching and the tendency to lean toward the right side. Consequently, the right hip appears higher than the left due to the right sideways lean of the body, which involves adducting the right hip and lengthening the right gluteus medius. This sideways lean may cause a slight deviation of the spine toward the left and force the left foot into more excessive pronation than the right foot. (5) Lack of dorsiflexion at the ankle joint usually is associated with overpronation. (6) Bowlegs, or varus, is a deviation associated with knee hyperextension and medial rotation of the hip. (7) Low-force, longer-duration static stretches evoke low-grade muscle spindle activity and a temporary increase in muscle tension due to muscle lengthening. This low-grade muscle response progressively decreases due to a gradual desensitization of the muscle spindle activity as the duration of the stretch progresses. After approximately seven to 10 seconds of a low-force stretch, the increase in muscle tension activates a Golgi tendon organ (GTO) response. Under GTO activation, muscle spindle activity within the stretched muscle is temporarily inhibited, allowing further muscle stretching. This concept defines autogenic inhibition.

II. (a) SW & FB; (b) KL & L; (c) KL, SW, & FB; (d) SW; (e) FB; (f) KL

III. (a) facilitation; (b) length-tension relationship; (c) 150 to 167%; (d) sarcomeres; (e) 51 to 55%; 13%; 21%; (f) 30 degrees; (g) four; teenage or young-adult years; (h) faulty neural control

IV. (1) The rectus abdominis pulling upward on the anterior, inferior pelvis; (2) The hip flexors pulling downward on the anterior, superior pelvis; (3) The hamstrings pulling downward on the posterior, inferior pelvis; (4) The erector spinae group pulling upward on the posterior, superior pelvis

V. To help determine the subtalar position, the ACE-AHFS can palpate the joint by placing the thumb and index finger immediately behind the tendons of the extensor hallucis longus and digitorum longus (immediately anterior to the malleoli). The ACE-AHFS should ask the client to maximally pronate and supinate the foot to determine which movement demonstrates a greater degree of movement. This indicates whether he or she normally stands more in pronation or supination.

VI. (1) Overpronation; (2) Internal rotation; hyperextension; (3) Anterior pelvic tilt; hip adduction (and lateral pelvic tilt) on dominant side; excessive pronation at the foot and internal rotation at the knees; (4) Excessive kyphosis and depressed chest; winging scapula or protracted scapula; internal rotation of the humerus; (5) Forward-head position

VII. (1) Examines bilateral mobility in the hips and lumbar spine during a forward bend and observes neural control and movement efficiency during the return from a forward bend. (2) Examines simultaneous mobility of one limb and stability of the contralateral (opposite) limb, while maintaining both hip and torso stabilization under a balance challenge of standing on one leg. (3) Examines hamstring and contralateral hip-flexor mobility while maintaining simultaneous trunk stability. (4) Examines active hamstring and lumbar stability, or active hamstring mobility without low-back compensation. (5) Examines hip flexor performance and lumbar stability without low-back compensation. (6) Examines bilateral mobility of the shoulder girdle and key upper-extremity muscle groups during overhead movement patterns.

VIII.

Restorative Progress Steps	Modality
Inhibit hypertonic muscles	Myofascial release, static stretching, PNF, isometric contractions, and active isolated stretches
Lengthen hypertonic muscles	Static stretching and PNF
Activation of latent muscles	Isometric contractions, active isolated stretches, muscle activation techniques, and dynamic contractions
Integration into functional movement	Part-to-whole progression of movement patterns

IX. The stretch-then-strengthen approach involves inhibiting and reducing tension in the hypertonic (tight) muscles, and stretching the tight muscles before strengthening the latent (weakened) muscles to facilitate their full activation.

X. It is critical that the ACE-AHFS understands how to "set" the scapulae to strengthen the necessary muscles in the correct neutral positions. In terms of posture, the scapulae are the "chief engineers" of the scapulothoracic region. The priority must be to facilitate retraction and depression of the scapulae using the surrounding musculature to return the posture to its origin.

Chapter 14

Mobility, Gait, and Balance

Expand Your Knowledge

I. (1) Muscle weakness; (2) A deconditioned core; (3) Reduced joint mobility; (4) Neurological losses; (5) Proprioceptive losses

II. (1) Anticipatory postural control involves stabilization of the body in anticipation of voluntary disruptive events that may require postural changes and potential losses in balance. (2) Reactive postural control occurs in response to unexpected threats to balance that cause the line of gravity to move away from the BOS. This control is necessary to restore balance and prevent a fall. If the disturbance does not exceed the LOS, the righting response may not require a change to the BOS, but if the disturbance is significantly large, it does require a change in BOS (e.g., taking a step or multiple steps to avoid a fall). (3) Adaptive postural control is the control of posture through the integration of afferent information from all three sensory systems and efferent (neuromuscular) commands. This allows the body to modify the sensory and motor systems in response to the environment and situational changes.

III. Maintaining balance relies on three distinct strategies utilized consciously or subconsciously. They involve the ankle, knee, and hip. Ankle strategies occur in response to small disturbances in balance to restore the COG within the BOS by action at the ankle joint. This strategy primarily involves activation of either the plantarflexors or dorsiflexors, resulting in simultaneous sway, or movement of the upper and lower body in the same direction to restore balance. Given the relative weakness of the musculature of the ankle, this strategy generates small amounts of force and responds to minimal balance disturbances, such as normal postural sway. Hip strategies occur in response to larger and/or faster disturbances in balance necessitating faster restorations of the COG within the BOS. Given the larger magnitude of correction required, the larger hip muscles are recruited to move the lower and upper extremities in opposite directions to restore balance. Knee or step strategies respond when ankle and hip strategies are ineffective in restoring balance, given that the balance disturbance has exceeded the body's static LOS. Movement is required in the direction of the disturbance by taking a step to restore balance under a new BOS without losing postural control. Knee or hip strategies are vital to maintaining dynamic balance during movement.

IV. (1) The deep layer, or inner unit, consists of small muscles (rotatores, interspinali, intertransversarii) that span single vertebra and are generally too small to offer stabilization of the entire spine. They offer segmental stabilization of each vertebra, especially at end ranges of motion, and are rich in sensory nerve endings that provide feedback information to the brain relating to spinal position. (2) The middle layer forms a box spanning several vertebrae, from the diaphragm to the pelvic floor, with muscles and fascia enclosing the back, front, and sides. The group consists of the transverse abdominis, multifidus, quadratus lumborum, posterior fibers of the internal oblique, the diaphragm, the pelvic floor musculature, and the adjoining fascia (i.e., linea alba, thoracolumbar fascia). This box allows the spine and sacroiliac joint to stiffen in anticipation of loading and movement, and provides a working foundation from which the body can operate. (3) The outer layer consists of big powerful muscles that span many vertebrae and are involved in gross movement of the trunk. These muscles include the rectus abdominis, erector spinae group, external and internal oblique, iliopsoas, and latissimus dorsi.

V. The transverse abdominis functions primarily to increase intra-abdominal pressure, reducing compressive forces along the spine. In healthy individuals, this muscle fires in anticipation of voluntary or involuntary loading of the spine to reduce compressive forces. Delayed or minimal activation of the transverse abdominis

muscle and limited co-contraction of core muscles has been observed in individuals suffering from low-back pain. Delayed onset of the transverse abdominis may cause inadequate stabilization of the lumbar spine during movements of the upper extremity.

VI. Abdominal hollowing is the isolated activation of the inner unit that draws the umbilicus inward and upward. Abdominal bracing involves the co-contraction of both the core and abdominal muscles to create a more rigid and wider BOS for spinal stabilization. While hollowing serves essential motor re-education purposes, it does not ensure the same degree of stability as bracing. Ultimately, clients should implement bracing, as it is a more effective method of stabilizing the spine.

VII. (1) Adequate ranges of motion in all necessary planes across the involved joints; (2) Adequate strength levels within each of the involved muscles; (3) Unimpaired sensory input from the visual, somatosensory, and vestibular systems; (4) Appropriate magnitude and timing of muscle activation and coordination

VIII. (1) Hip abductors eccentrically prevent excessive lateral pelvic tilting, the knee extensors eccentrically prevent excessive flexion, and the ankle dorsiflexors eccentrically control plantarflexion. This results in weight acceptance, pelvic stabilization, and deceleration. (2) Hip abductors and adductors stabilize hip and knee alignment over the foot, the gastrocnemius helps stabilize the knee, the contralateral quadratus lumborum controls lateral pelvic tilting, and the plantarflexors eccentrically control tibial advancement over the foot. (3) The loaded hip extensor and contralateral arm begin to control rotation and ready the body for propulsion. (4) The loaded hip extensor and contralateral arm provide propulsion and the hip flexors initiate hip flexion. (5) Ankle dorsiflexors act concentrically to help clear the foot. (6) Ankle dorsiflexors eccentrically control plantarflexion, the hamstrings act eccentrically to slow knee extension, and the contralateral erector spinae group stabilizes the sacroiliac joint and maintains trunk extension in preparation for initial contact.

IX. Force closure, or stabilization, relates to the ability of the muscle system, through its attachments into connective tissue (systems of myofascial slings), to compress the joint surfaces of the sacrum and iliac bones together. During gait, ground reactive forces transmit superiorly, while the force of gravity transmits forces inferiorly. While these myofascial slings facilitate efficient movement and help stabilize joints, they buffer forces, distributing them throughout the kinetic chain. These slings are defined as the posterior longitudinal, or deep longitudinal, system; the lateral system; the anterior oblique system; and the posterior oblique system.

X. (1) Single-leg movements (single-leg stance); (2) Squatting movements (bending and lifting); (3) Pushing movements (in vertical and horizontal planes); (4) Pulling movements (in vertical and horizontal planes); (5) Rotational movements

XI. Men typically have a Q-angle of 13 degrees, whereas women have a Q-angle of 18 degrees. A wider pelvis, coupled with shorter bones, exaggerates the Q-angle in women, leading to greater knee instability. Additionally, greater joint laxity, smaller ligaments and surface area for attachment, and weaker muscles all compound the potential for knee injury in women.

XII. (a) IADL; (b) IADL; (c) BADL; (d) AADL; (e) IADL; (f) BADL; (g) AADL

XIII. (1) Restoring good posture (restorative exercises addressing correctable compensations through stretching and strengthening); (2) Re-educating faulty neural pathways of the core musculature; (3) Developing static and basic dynamic balance; (4) Enhancing sensory acuity and postural control strategies; (5) Improving gait patterns and more advanced dynamic balance

XIV. (1) Re-educate the neural pathways and activate the core muscles with no, or minimal, engagement of the rectus abdominis or hip flexors (i.e., no movement of the hips and torso). The goal is to learn the concept of centering, or "drawing in." (2) Introduce small balance challenges that reflexively engage the muscles under smaller spinal loads while the body is held in a static position. (3) Introduce the concept of bracing for greater spinal stability in both static and dynamic environments. The exercises transition from static to dynamic movement through various stance positions and with various surfaces. (4) Develop endurance of the core musculature and strength within the outer muscle layers to effectively tolerate dynamic forces in multiple planes of movement. (5) Improve neuromuscular control of the core during explosive movements, which are introduced during this stage and are generally only recommended for well-conditioned individuals.

XV. (1) Perception of the activity or awareness of volitional muscle activity, joint position, and movement; (2) Feedback during and following activity, as the cognitive and nervous systems evaluate performance and make any necessary adjustments; (3) Perfect repetitions with increasing accuracy as mastery increases, potentially decreasing the required effort and overflow from other muscles; (4) The ability to inhibit undesired muscle activity and response is facilitated by precise, slow and controlled movement until engrams are developed, after which speed and intensity can be increased.

Chapter 15

Arthritis

Expand Your Knowledge

I. (1) Rheumatoid arthritis is a chronic autoimmune disease that results in inflammation of the synovium, leading to long-term joint damage, chronic pain, and loss of function or disability. Osteoarthritis results from a degeneration of synovial fluid and generally progresses into a loss of articular cartilage, which typically presents itself as localized joint pain and a reduction of range of motion. (2) If the underlying cause for a health problem cannot be identified, the condition falls into the primary etiology category (i.e., the individual has the problem, but physicians cannot determine why or what is causing or contributing to the problem). If the underlying cause that contributed to the onset of the condition and/or continues to contribute to the condition can be identified, the condition is categorized as secondary. (3) Injuries that are a result of a singular traumatic event are called acute, whereas injuries that are a result of trauma over a prolonged period of time are considered to have an insidious onset. (4) Type A synovial cells are secretory in that they produce the synovial fluid that acts as a lubricant for the joint. The type B synovial cells are phagocytic, in that they are responsible for the debridement (removal) of the "worn out" synovial fluid and any excess fluid (synovial fluid and/or blood) that may have accumulated in the joint. (5) The joint capsule fully encloses a joint, so that fluid produced in the joint is retained in the joint. Lining the capsule is a synovial membrane that consists of synovial cells. (6) Grade 1 articular damage implies only superficial changes to the articular cartilage, whereas grade 4 articular damage implies damage to the point where subchondral bone is exposed.

II. (1) The first phase involves swelling of the synovial lining, resulting in pain, warmth, stiffness, redness, and swelling of the joint.

(2) The second phase is a rapid division and growth of cells, which causes the synovium to thicken. (3) In the third and final phase, the inflamed cells release enzymes that break down bone and cartilage, causing the affected joint to lose structure and alignment, leading to more pain and a further decrease in function.

III. (1) The condition of the articular cartilage, which consists of hyaline cartilage, that covers the portions of bone that articulate with each other within a joint. (2) The status of the subchondral bone that underlies the articular cartilage, which must be healthy to provide appropriate structural support to the articular cartilage overlying it. (3) Discomfort and/or swelling.

IV. (1) When the surface of articular cartilage is pristine and covered with synovial fluid, the coefficient of friction between two articulating surfaces is almost zero. (2) Because it lacks pain fibers, the articular cartilage prevents the subchondral bone, which has an abundance of pain fibers, from experiencing pain related to the normal transmission of force across joints on a daily basis. (3) Healthy articular cartilage can tolerate approximately seven times the person's body weight before undesirable and often silent detrimental changes begin to compromise the structural integrity of the articular cartilage.

V. Initial changes to the articular cartilage involve the changing of the once pristine surface into an uneven, incongruous surface. These changes can occur quickly from acute trauma, such as a torn anterior cruciate ligament, meniscal tear, or dislocated patella. Each of these injuries produce shear forces in the joint that damage the articular cartilage. The loss of the pristine surfaces leads to an increase in the coefficient of friction, which hastens damage due to wear and tear on the remaining articular cartilage. Along with the loss of the pristine surface, the once microscopic pores that allowed the synovial fluid to flow freely into the articular cartilage become enlarged, allowing the escape of chemicals from inside the articular cartilage into the joint. These chemicals are direct irritants to the synovial cells and cause them to become inflamed (chemical synovitis). Once inflamed, the cells produce soreness throughout the knee as well as an excessive amount of synovial fluid, which is experienced as tightness in the knee. With the continuous wear-and-tear changes due to the increased coefficient of friction, the articular cartilage becomes thinner, allowing the subchondral bone to experience more of the forces transmitted across the joint. Further progression leads to bone-on-bone contact and constant pain.

VI. (1) Joint pain; (2) Over 50 years of age; (3) Less than 30 minutes of morning joint stiffness; (4) Crepitus; (5) Bony tenderness; (6) Bony enlargement; (7) No palpable warmth of synovium; (8) Erythrocyte sedimentation rate (ESR) <40 mm/hr; (9) Rheumatoid factor <1:40; (10) Non-inflammatory synovial fluid

VII. 1) Any individual who has had surgery on a joint involved in the exercise program; (2) Individuals who state that they experience discomfort and/or tightness the day following physical activity; (3) Overweight individuals; (4) Individuals who walk with an altered gait, especially following participation in a weightbearing activity; (5) Individuals who feel the need to wear a brace with activity

VIII. While there is no cure for osteoarthritis, maintaining a regular exercise program of resistance and aerobic training can reduce the pain and rate of decline in functional capacity. No evidence exists that properly programmed and managed exercise will increase the rate of joint degeneration, as measured by joint-space narrowing. Exercise can help reduce some of the risk factors associated with the progression of osteoarthritis, including weak quadriceps, valgus or varus knee alignment, weak hip abductors, and obesity. By selecting exercises or developing programs that address these conditions, an ACE-AHFS can help reduce pain and functional limitations, as well as slow the progression of osteoarthritis to keep clients active. Further reductions in quadriceps strength, as well as in the hip abductors and extensors, will accelerate the deterioration of the joint by reducing the ability of the individual to control anterior-posterior motion of the knee, as well as exacerbating structural alignment problems that may lead to asymmetrical wear on the articular cartilage.

IX. (a) 80%; 25%; (b) knees; hips; spine; hands; feet; (c) trauma; obesity; (d) blood supply; pain fibers; (e) stiffness of the joint from chemical synovitis: (f) anti-inflammatory medications; glucosamine sulfate

Show What You Know

After receiving medical clearance for Beth for her elevated blood pressure and discomfort in her knees, the ACE-AHFS should encourage Beth to engage in a comprehensive exercise program to improve her quality of life, mobility, and general health. Beth should perform cardiorespiratory exercise three to five days per week (or more if tolerated, due to her elevated blood pressure) of light- to moderate-intensity (50–70% HRR) of aquatic exercise for 30 to 60 continuous minutes. However, an option of multiple, shorter sessions per day should be available to help reduce joint pain. For resistance training, Beth can begin with isometric exercises or light resistance to strengthen the quadriceps, hamstrings, and gluteals without putting undue pressure on her joints. A frequency of two to three days of resistance training per week is an appropriate goal. These exercises can also be performed in a pool to further reduce joint pressures. Beth should progress to bodyweight bilateral exercises (e.g., squats) to develop overall muscular and joint control while encouraging full ROM. She can add external resistance to increase muscular strength and endurance if she is pain free. Beth can then progress to unilateral exercises (lunges, step-ups) to develop muscular control of the joint complex. She should focus on proper control and technique to make sure the patella and femur track correctly. Lastly, Beth should perform flexibility exercises daily to keep her joints mobile and compliant. She should perform dynamic flexibility exercises to increase range of motion and keep her joints lubricated, and static stretching to decrease passive tension (emphasis on the hamstrings, quadriceps, gluteals, gastrocnemius, soleus, and adductors for the lower extremity, and the pectorals, trapezius, latissimus dorsi, deltoids, rhomboids, rotator cuff muscles, biceps, and triceps for the upper extremity).

Chapter 16

Osteoporosis and Osteopenia

Expand Your Knowledge

I. (a) 5; (b) 3; (c) 2; (d) 6; (e) 1; (f) 4; (g) 7; (h) 10; (i) 9; (j) 8

II. (1) Bone mineral is accrued at various rates throughout early childhood and adolescence, and then diminishes with aging. This normal, age-related process causes a net loss of approximately 5 to 10% of bone mineral per decade and begins some time after the cessation of longitudinal growth and the achievement of peak bone mass. (2) Bone resorption in women is especially rapid during the first five years following menopause (if pharmacotherapy is not implemented), and may cause a loss of 3 to 5% of overall bone mass per year. These age-related bone mineral decrements are not as clinically significant in men, primarily because men reach a higher peak BMD, have larger bones that afford a biomechanical resistance to fracture, and do not experience the same rapid postmenopausal bone loss as women. (3) BMD appears to be controlled by a combination of several genes, which may also display important interactive effects with environmental factors (such as physical activity and calcium intake). BMD is strongly influenced by parental bone mass and research shows very little variation in BMD between identical twins. (4) Compared with whites, black adults have higher BMD at both the hip and spine and an increased cortical thickness. Lower fracture rates at both the hip and spine have also been reported. Although rates of bone loss appear similar for black and white individuals, it is estimated that African-American women have a 50% lower risk of fracture than Caucasian women. Similar lower fracture rates have also been shown for Hispanic and Asian populations. (5) Estrogen has both direct and indirect effects on bone. Directly, estrogen decreases bone remodeling (turnover) through a complex interaction with the estrogen receptor on osteoblasts and by inhibiting other hormones that would normally stimulate osteoclast production. In this way, estrogen maintains bone mass by limiting resorption. Estrogen may also exhibit indirect effects on bone through the parathyroid gland, gut, and kidneys. Specifically, estrogen may lower the sensitivity of parathyroid hormone (PTH) to serum calcium levels that would promote mineralization by reducing bone turnover. It may also increase reabsorption of calcium via the kidneys by stimulating vitamin D and calcitonin production, which would also limit bone turnover. (6) Smoking has a detrimental effect on both pre- and postmenopausal bone density via an increased bone resorption and decreased calcium absorption. (7) Excessive alcohol consumption appears to exert a direct toxic effect on bone, whereas moderate alcohol consumption may be associated with a slight increase in bone via increases in estradiol concentrations. (8) Caffeine increases urinary excretion of calcium for at least three hours after ingestion and has been associated with changes in bone remodeling. It does appear that calcium balance decreases with every cup of coffee ingested, but that these effects are offset by calcium intake. Carbonated cola beverages, on the other hand, do not appear to adversely affect short-term calcium balance, although more studies are needed in this area, since it is possible that the phosphorus contained in these beverages may adversely affect bone. (9) Dietary calcium provides the essential building blocks for bone formation. Without an adequate daily intake, calcium is withdrawn from the bones to maintain normal blood levels. Adequate calcium intake is especially important during growth, when the skeleton is still forming and prior to the fourth decade of life when peak bone mass may still be influenced. If vitamin D levels are insufficient, parathyroid hormone secretion is increased, which increases activity of the bone-resorbing osteoclasts.

III. The term "female athlete triad" describes a condition consisting of a combination of disordered eating, menstrual irregularities, and decreased bone mass in athletic women. This combination of factors may increase a woman's risk of osteoporosis and premature fracture. Dieting behavior usually becomes very restrictive and the pathogenic weight-control behaviors predispose a woman to menstrual dysfunction and eventually compromised bone mass. This is most likely due to a combination of low estrogen and, more importantly, chronic undernutrition that reduces the rate of bone formation.

IV. (1) A change in periods—shorter or longer, lighter or heavier, with more or less time in between; (2) Hot flashes and/or night sweats; (3) Trouble sleeping; (4) Vaginal dryness; (5) Mood swings; (6) Trouble

focusing; (7) Less hair on the head and more on the face

V. 1) All women aged 65 and older regardless of risk factors; (2) Younger postmenopausal women with one or more risk factors (other than being white, postmenopausal, and female); (3) Postmenopausal women who present with fractures (to confirm the diagnosis and determine disease severity)

VI. (a) QUS; (b) QCT; (c) DEXA; (d) DEXA; (e) QCT; (f) QUS; (g) DEXA

VII. (1) Calcitonin is a hormone that inhibits osteoclastic activity, thus reducing bone resorption. Calcitonin has shown effectiveness in both increasing low bone mass and decreasing fracture risk in postmenopausal women. (2) Bisphosphonates, another class of antiresorptives, are generally well tolerated, although they may cause gastrointestinal intolerance in some individuals. It is very important that clients remain upright for at least 30 minutes following oral dosing to avoid esophageal discomfort. They function by inhibiting the action of osteoclasts (formation remains the same), thereby slowing bone resorption. (3) SERMs represent a class of agents that, while similar in structure to estrogen, exert their effects only on target tissues. The most studied is raloxifene (Evista®); its effects on markers of bone turnover have been more modest than with bisphosphonates, and its effect on non-vertebral fractures such as the hip have not been significant. (4) Parathyroid hormone is an anabolic hormone that, unlike antiresorptive drugs that reduce bone resorption, acts mainly to stimulate bone formation. (5) Strontium ranelate is an antiosteoporotic agent that is used in the European Union but is not yet approved for use in the U.S. Although its exact mechanism is unclear, it is the first drug that apparently increased bone formation while also reducing bone resorption.

VIII. (1) The best time to load bone is prior to puberty. Improvements in bone mass during this time are more dramatic and they may cause an increase in peak bone mass that persists into adulthood. (2) Bone requires dynamic, rather than static, loads to improve its size, shape, and/or density. (3) Bone requires loads over and above normal daily loading to improve its size, shape, and/or density. Bone must sense an overload stimulus if it is to adapt. Higher stresses produce higher bone strains, and these can be accomplished by higher force magnitudes and/or faster application of force. (4) Bone's response is proportional to strain frequency. Bone is maintained both with less frequent mechanical loads of higher intensity and with higher frequency loads at lower intensity. (5) Bone's response is improved with brief, intermittent exercise, and may require six to eight hours of recovery between intense loading sessions. The number of loads need not be high (anywhere from five to 50 impacts can be beneficial) to produce the desired response. (6) Bone requires an unusual loading pattern to improve. Exercise that loads the skeleton in unusual, uncustomary ways, produces more dramatic responses than those using normal loading patterns.

IX. (1) Several bouts of bone-loading exercise are more effective than one long bout. (2) High-intensity activities with high strain rates promote stronger bones than endurance-type activities. (3) The number of strain cycles can be small (e.g., 50 to 100), so the duration can be short (five to 10 minutes depending on the types of activities chosen). (4) A variety of loading patterns applied in unusual ways is more beneficial than activities that mimic everyday activities. Static loads (e.g., isometrics) do not promote increased bone accrual.

X. Performing strength-training exercises in a standing, weightbearing position will challenge the vestibular system, involve stabilizing muscles, and translate to activities of daily living (ADL) much more effectively than seated activities. This type of exercise may also help prevent falls in this population by enhancing balance.

XI. A regular walking program, combined with resistance training that targets balance and upper- and lower-body muscle strength, may help to improve muscle strength and coordination in individuals with osteoporosis, thereby reducing fall risk. Each exercise session should begin with an eight- to 15-minute warm-up of gentle stretching and range-of-motion exercises, followed by resistance exercise, and conclude with five to 10 minutes of aerobic activity at 60 to 75% of maximum predicted heart rate. Clients diagnosed with osteoporosis, with or without a history of vertebral fractures, should not engage in jumping activities or deep forward trunk flexion exercises such as rowing, toe touches, and full sit-ups.

Show What You Know

Olivia should be encouraged to quit smoking, since cigarette smoking is associated with an increase in bone resorption and decreased calcium absorption. Quitting smoking may also help her gain body weight, as her low BMI (17.5 kg/m^2) increases her risk for fracture. Olivia should remain cognizant of the recommended daily intake of 1200 to 1500 mg of calcium and 400 IU of vitamin D to counteract her caffeine consumption and promote BMD maintenance. She should be encouraged to eat a variety of food sources containing calcium and use the National Osteoporosis Foundation's website (www.nof.org) as a useful guide to assist in estimating calcium intake.

Chapter 17

Principles of Post-orthopedic Rehabilitation

Expand Your Knowledge

I. Obtaining as much information as possible, both subjective and objective, regarding the client's health will help establish a strong foundation for making exercise program development successful for the client. In particular, obtaining information from the new medical team members regarding the precautions and contraindications related to exercise is crucial, especially in orthopedic rehabilitation. Doing so will help protect the client from re-injury or any regression of the medical condition, which could damage the ACE-AHFS's relationship with not only the medical team, but also the client and future referred clients.

II. Questioning a client regarding his or her level of pain or discomfort during this initial interview is important for developing safe exercise programming. A client's description of his or her pain will help the ACE-AHFS decipher if it is due to normal physical stress (such as muscle soreness), injury, disease, or some other type of pathology. It will also help lead to a discussion regarding what type of activities or circumstances exacerbate the pain or discomfort versus ones that provide relief. This type of exchange will provide valuable information on what exercises can be tolerated by the client. Throughout the duration of the program, exacerbation of pain or other signs and symptoms warrant immediate adjustments, and communication with the medical team is mandatory to formulate a plan for continued safe participation in an exercise program.

III. Maintaining a current file of established rehabilitation protocols by diagnosis will be an invaluable resource to the

ACE-AHFS, who can learn from them and refer to them while working with clients. Rehabilitation protocols provide structure for a client's exercise program, as well as guidance for progressing the program at any point in a client's recovery. Additionally, these protocols can effectively serve as conversation "icebreakers" with medical professionals if a client is not able to see the medical professionals due to a lack of insurance or because of other prohibitive reasons. Requesting advice and accepting it from fellow medical team members by obtaining these protocols promotes trust and support and demonstrates a commitment to the best interests of the client. The ACE-AHFS will earn respect from all involved and will receive an increase in client referrals because of the high level of professionalism displayed by adopting such an approach.

IV.

Phase	Description	Objective	Duration
Inflammation	Immediately post-injury, the area shows signs of warmth, redness, inflammation swelling, and pain	Care for injury and control inflammation	1 day–1 week
Proliferation	Development of scar tissue that lays down with random orientation; increased girth due to edema	Clear necrotic tissue; begin tissue and cell regeneration to improve circulation	1–4 weeks
Remodeling	Scar tissue edema decreases, but density increases; signs and symptoms reduce; tissue fully fuses	Reestablish function of tissue, skeletal muscle, and joint in the area	1–12 months

V. Healthy tissue with less structural stiffness responds differently to stretching activities than unhealthy contracture, or scar, tissue. In general, tissue increases in length when it undergoes a static stretch of low magnitude for a prolonged period of time (15 to 30 seconds), when it reaches the plastic range and remodels to a new length. Shorter-duration stretches result in a return of this tissue to its original, pre-stretch length, as it only reaches its elastic range. Tissue that has been lacerated, either surgically or non-surgically, and has scar tissue forming around it will benefit from a significantly longer period of low-load, static stretching lasting minutes, due to increased bonding of collagen fibers. This effect on the tissue—called "creep"—elongates the tissue over time, influencing the scar tissue to deform permanently, resulting in greater flexibility.

VI. Cardiorespiratory training allows the smooth muscle of the heart to contract with greater force, allowing more blood to be pumped through the body with fewer heart beats per minute, bringing more oxygen and nutrients throughout the body more efficiently. Thus, improving a client's basic cardiovascular condition through a variety of aerobic endurance exercises will improve the health of various physiologic systems (e.g., cardiovascular, digestive, immune, respiratory). In addition, the client's heart rate, blood pressure, and respiratory rate will decrease, while muscle tone, energy storage, and aerobic system capacity will increase. This aerobic enhancement will also improve a client's perception of well-being by increasing his or her functional abilities, as well as psychological and emotional stability.

VII. (1) Improve the body's active range of motion and flexibility; (2) Enhance general conditioning and endurance; (3) Reintegrate clients into physical activity, recreation programs, and wellness; (4) Improve strength for competitive sports and manual labor challenges

Chapter 18

Musculoskeletal Injuries of the Lower Extremity

Expand Your Knowledge

I. (1) How did the injury happen (i.e., the mechanism of injury)? (2) Did you see your physician? If yes, what treatment has been done (e.g., surgery, physical therapy, oral medications, cortisone injection)? (3) Did the physician issue any exercise precautions or contraindications (e.g., limit walking to 15 minutes)? (4) What type of symptoms are you feeling (e.g., "sharp" pain when walking on the treadmill)? (5) Do you have any functional limitations (e.g., unable to lift objects overhead)? (6) What is your tolerance to activity (e.g., "feeling fatigue" after 10 minutes of treadmill walking)?

II. OKC exercises are non-weightbearing, with the distal end (e.g., the foot) free, and involve isolating a specific muscle group. CKC exercises have the distal end fixed and are typically more functional. CKC exercises are often thought to be superior due to joint compression, muscle co-contraction, and increased functionality.

III. Proprioception is a person's awareness of his or her body in space. Balance is dependent on sensory receptors, which are located in muscles, skin, tendons, ligaments, and joints. The central nervous system (CNS) receives input from these receptors along with visual and vestibular input, which are used to control body position and balance. When injury occurs, these pathways can be diminished due to trauma or disuse, which leads to poor balance and increased risk for injury. Retraining these pathways is necessary to maintain adequate neuromuscular control during functional and athletic activities. Proprioceptive exercises must be specific to the activity and should follow a graduated progression that includes the following principles: slow to fast, low force to high force, and controlled to uncontrolled movement.

IV. (1) (a) Inflammation of the trochanteric bursa may be due to an acute incident or repetitive trauma. Acute incidents may include trauma from falls, contact sports, and other sources of impact. Repetitive trauma may be due to excessive friction by the iliotibial band (ITB). This condition is more common in female runners, cross country skiers, and ballet dancers. Factors such as prolonged running, an increase or change in activity, leg-length discrepancy, and lateral hip surgery have been described as causes of repetitive trauma. (b) Trochanteric bursitis pain and/or paresthesias often radiate from the greater trochanter to the posterior lateral hip, down the iliotibial tract, to the lateral knee. Symptoms are most often related to an increase in activity or repetitive overuse. Aggravating activities may include lying on the affected side, prolonged walking/running, and certain hip movements (internal and external rotation). Deficits in hip strength, ROM, and gait may be present secondary to the pain. The client may walk with a limp due to pain or weakness. He or she may develop a compensation pattern through the painful limb that directly affects the lower kinetic chain. This may result in decreased muscle length, myofascial tightness, and weak, inhibited muscles. (c) There are no direct precautions for trochanteric bursitis. Clients are advised to avoid any aggravating activities and return to activity in a slow, systematic manner. (2) (a) ITBFS is a repetitive overuse condition that occurs when the distal portion of the iliotibial band rubs against the lateral femoral epicondyle. The repeated flexion and extension of the knee causes the ITB to pass back and forth over the lateral femoral epicondyle, leading to irritation and inflammation. ITBFS is common among active individuals 15 to 50 years of age and is primarily caused by training errors during various activities (e.g., running, cycling, playing volleyball, and weightlifting). Risk factors may include overtraining, changes in running surface, structural abnormalities (pes planus, bow-legs, and leg-length discrepancy), muscle imbalance, and muscle tightness. (b) Clients with ITBFS often report a gradual onset of tightness, burning, or pain at the lateral aspect of the knee during activity. The pain may be localized, but generally radiates to the outside of the knee and/or up the outside of the thigh. Snapping, popping, or pain may be felt at the lateral knee when it is flexed and extended. Aggravating factors may include any repetitive activity such as running (especially downhill) or cycling. The client may present with weakness in the hip abductors, ITB shortening, and tenderness throughout the ITB complex. (c) There are no direct precautions for ITBFS. Clients are advised to avoid any aggravating activities and return to activity in a slow, systematic manner. (3) (a) OA develops from the degeneration of joint cartilage and supporting structures, and changes in the underlying bone structure. This degeneration is caused by a physiologic imbalance between the stress applied to the joint and the ability of the joint to endure the stress. Simply put, osteoarthritis develops when breakdown exceeds re-growth. (b) OA leads to stiffness, pain, mobility problems, and limited physical activity. A client with hip OA may complain of a "deep aching" pain in the anterior hip with weightbearing activity and "stiffness" after inactivity (less than 30 minutes). The client may have activity limitations due to restricted, painful motion or a feeling of instability. The hip joint may be tender to touch, swollen, and have crepitation. (c) Clients with hip OA must limit prolonged weightbearing activities, shock loading (e.g., running), and repetitive squatting. Specific activities to avoid include deep squats or lunges, knee extensions, and plyometric activity. Light-to-moderate activity is recommended due to the diminished shock-absorbing capacity of the joint. (4) (a) Total hip replacement is commonly done to correct intractable damage from osteoarthritis, rheumatoid arthritis, hip fractures, avascular necrosis, and cerebral palsy. When conservative approaches have failed, replacing the joint is often the best option. (b) Typically, the client has suffered with a painful, stiff joint for some time and may have tried conservative treatment such as oral medications, injections, and physical therapy. (c) In general, high-impact activities such as running, football, basketball, soccer, karate, water skiing, and racquetball should be avoided following total hip replacement. These activities may cause abnormal stress to the prosthetic joint. For clients who have undergone the posterior lateral approach, the precautions are hip flexion greater than 90 degrees, hip adduction past the midline of the body, and hip internal rotation past neutral. The precautions associated with the anterior lateral approach are combined hip external rotation and flexion, hip adduction past the midline of the body, and hip internal rotation beyond neutral. Hyperextension of the hip and extreme hip external rotation are precautions for the anterior approach. (5) (a) PFPS is often classified as an overuse syndrome when repetitive loading activities or sports are the cause of symptoms. These repetitive activities cause abnormal stress to the knee joint, which leads to pain and dysfunction. The excessive loading exceeds the body's physiological balance, which leads to tissue trauma, injury, and pain. Recent changes in intensity, frequency, duration, and training environment may contribute to this condition. Biomechanical causes such as pes planus, pes cavus, and a large Q-angle have also been reported. (b) Commonly reported symptoms include pain with running, stair climbing, squatting, or prolonged sitting

(e.g., theater sign). The client will typically describe a gradual "achy" pain that occurs behind or underneath the knee cap and may be immediate if trauma has occurred. Clients may also report knee stiffness, giving way, clicking, or a popping sensation during movement. (c) The client is encouraged to avoid high-stress activities such as running, repetitive squatting, prolonged sitting, and stair climbing. Also, certain OKC exercises (e.g., leg extensions) have been known to cause abnormal stress on the patellofemoral joint. (6) (a) Meniscal injuries often occur from trauma or degeneration. Traumatic injuries can occur from a combination of loading and twisting of the joint. The combination of axial loading with pivoting of the femur on the tibia causes a shear force across the meniscus that exceeds the strength of the tissue, resulting in injury. Older individuals with degenerative menisci are more predisposed to meniscal tears. Meniscal tears can also occur with other traumatic injuries such as acute ACL tears or medial collateral ligament injury. (b) When a client has a meniscal tear, he or she may complain of symptoms during activity. Commonly reported symptoms include stiffness, clicking or popping with joint loading, giving way, catching, and locking (in more severe tears). Other signs include joint pain, swelling, and muscle weakness. (c) Frequently with non-operative management, clients will be cleared to resume activity once symptoms have diminished, but they are encouraged to avoid deep squats, cutting, pivoting, or twisting for as long as symptoms are present. (7) (a) The mechanism of injury often involves a maneuver of deceleration combined with twisting, pivoting, or side-stepping. The combined multiplanar movements cause a traumatic shearing force that exceeds the tensile strength of the ACL, resulting in injury. (b) An ACL injury is often traumatic. The client will often report hearing a "pop" during the activity, followed by immediate swelling, instability, decreased ROM, and pain. This typically requires immediate medical care to immobilize and protect the joint, followed by a visit to the orthopedic doctor for further diagnosis and intervention. (c) With non-operative management, the client may be cleared to slowly resume activity once symptoms have diminished, but may be restricted from performing jumping, cutting, pivoting, or twisting motions. Wearing a protective knee brace is recommended to protect the deficient knee during activity. Post-surgical precautions dictate that the knee should be gradually introduced to activity to allow adaptation and adequate healing. To protect the graft, the physician may have the client wear a protective brace for the first year after surgery or permanently during activity. Activity should be stopped if any of the following occurs: increased pain at the surgical site, increased swelling, loss of ROM, and increased exercise pain. (8) (a) TKR is indicated when conservative treatment fails to restore mobility or reduce arthritic pain, chronic knee inflammation, or swelling. (b) Similar to a client coping with an arthritic hip, the TKR client has suffered with a painful joint for some time and may have tried conservative treatment such as oral medication, injections, and physical therapy. (c) There are no specific movement precautions for these procedures. The client is encouraged to avoid high-stress activities such as jogging, skiing, tennis, racquetball, jumping, repetitive squatting, and contact sports. Until cleared, lifting is typically limited to no more than 40 pounds and heavy weightlifting is discouraged. (9) (a) Lateral, or inversion, ankle sprains are the most common type of ankle sprain. The mechanism is typically inversion with a plantarflexed foot. The lateral ankle ligaments are the most common structures involved, including the anterior talofibular ligament (ATFL), calcaneofibular ligament

(CFL), and posterior talofibular ligament (PTFL). Medial, or eversion, ankle sprains result from forced dorsiflexion and eversion of the ankle. The medial deltoid ligament is the most common structure involved and injury often requires further examination to rule out a fracture. (b) With lateral ankle sprains, the individual can often recall the mechanism and hearing a "pop" or "tearing" sound. A first degree ankle sprain involves the ATFL ligament, with pain and mild swelling over the lateral aspect of the ankle. Typically, weightbearing is tolerable after injury. A second degree ankle sprain involves both the ATFL and CFL ligaments, with more severe pain and swelling over the lateral ankle. Weightbearing may be limited due to pain. A third degree ankle sprain is considered a complete tear of one or more of the lateral ligaments. Rapid, severe pain, swelling, and discoloration occur and individuals are unable to bear weight. Medial ankle sprains rarely happen in isolation. The individual is often unable to recall the specific mechanism, but can reproduce discomfort by dorsiflexing and everting the ankle. There may be medial swelling with tenderness over the deltoid ligament. (c) The client may be cleared to slowly resume activity once symptoms have diminished. He or she is encouraged to wear the appropriate ankle bracing and to avoid lateral and multiplane movements until cleared by a physician. These movements may put the client at risk for further injury and should be introduced when appropriate. (10) (a) There have been several intrinsic and extrinsic risk factors associated with this condition. Intrinsic factors include pes planus, pes cavus, and decreased strength and poor flexibility of the calf muscles. Extrinsic factors include overtraining, improper footwear, obesity, and unforgiving and hard surfaces. Any of these factors can cause excessive loading of the plantar fascia, leading to pain and dysfunction. (b) Typically, individuals report pain on the plantar, medial heel at its calcaneal attachment that worsens after rest, but improves after 10 to 15 minutes of activity. In particular, clients will commonly report excessive pain during the first few steps in the morning. Clients may also have stiffness and muscle spasms in the lower leg with tightness in the Achilles tendon. (c) Individuals with plantar fasciitis may be limited in their activity due to pain. Activities that excessively load the fascia, such as running or jumping, should be avoided due to exacerbation of the condition. The condition can be challenging due to the pain relief that occurs with basic activity and the recurrence of symptoms after rest. The ACE-AHFS needs to monitor changes in symptoms and refer the client to the appropriate medical professional, if necessary. (11) (a) Various intrinsic and extrinsic factors are associated with Achilles tendinopathy. Intrinsic factors include age, bodyweight, pes cavus, pes planus, leg-length discrepancies, and lateral ankle instability. Extrinsic factors include errors in training, prior injuries, poor footwear, muscle weakness, and poor flexibility. The extrinsic factors are typically responsible for acute tendon trauma. (b) Individuals often complain of pain that is 0.75 to 2.25 inches above the tendon insertion into the calcaneus. The typical pattern is initial morning pain that is "sharp" or "burning," as well as pain with more vigorous activity. Rest will often alleviate the pain, but as the condition becomes worse, the pain becomes more constant and begins to interfere with activities of daily living. (c) Clients with Achilles tendinopathy are encouraged to stop all aggravating activity and seek proper treatment for the condition. High-loading activities such as jumping, running, and stair climbing should be avoided until the condition has improved. (12) (a) Shin splints are typically classified as two specific conditions: medial tibial stress

syndrome (MTSS) and anterior shin splints. MTSS, also called posterior shin splints, is an overuse injury that occurs in the active population. MTSS is an exercise-induced condition that is often triggered by a sudden change in activity. MTSS is actually periostitis, or inflammation of the periosteum of the bone. Originally, this condition was thought to be caused by posterior tibial tendinitis. It has since been related to a traction periostitis at the distal insertion of the soleus muscle or from the flexor digitorum longus muscle. MTSS has been most frequently associated with pes planus. Excessive overpronation of the foot during activity produces an eccentric stress to the muscles that results in a painful periostitis. The etiology of anterior shin splints is not completely known, but the condition is often associated with exertional activity. Both MTSS and anterior shin splints have been associated with overtraining, poor footwear, changes in running surface, muscle weakness, and poor flexibility. (b) Clients commonly complain of a "dull ache" along the distal two thirds of the posterior medial tibia for MTSS and the distal anterior shin for anterior shin splints. The pain is elicited by initial activity, but diminishes as activity continues. The pain typically returns hours after activity. If the condition progresses, the pain becomes constant and tends to restrict performance. (c) Clients are encouraged to stop all aggravating activity and rest. Repetitive loading activities such as running and jumping are discouraged until symptoms have resolved. The client should be referred to his or her physician if this condition has not resolved within one or two months after initiation of modified activity and proper intervention. It is important for the ACE-AHFS to monitor symptoms during activity and refer the client to the doctor if there is no improvement, as a stress fracture must be ruled out. Stress fractures of the tibia can have similar signs and symptoms as shin splints.

V . (1) In a primary hip replacement, the whole joint is replaced with three components: a synthetic cup that replaces the acetabulum (plastic, ceramic, or metal); a ball that replaces the femoral head (highly polished metal or ceramic material); and a metal stem that is secured in the medullary canal of the proximal femur. (2) A hemiarthroplasty, or partial hip replacement, involves only half of the joint and includes replacing the ball portion of the joint, but not the socket portion. This procedure is commonly used to treat hip fractures or avascular necrosis of the hip. (3) For younger active individuals (less than 55 years of age), hip resurfacing can be done. This procedure includes resurfacing and reshaping only the femoral head with a shell or cap. Hip resurfacing is a common alternative to primary total hip replacement because it leaves more of the bone in place and does not remove the femoral neck shaft. Therefore, the procedure may give the patient more time before having to replace the whole joint.

VI. (1) Avoiding aggravating activities (e.g., prolonged sitting, deep squats, and running); (2) Modifying training techniques (e.g., frequency, intensity); (3) Proper footwear; (4) Physical therapy; (5) Patellar taping; (6) Knee bracing; (7) Arch supports; (8) Foot orthotics; (9) Patient education; (10) Oral anti-inflammatory medication; (11) Modalities (e.g., ice, heat)

VII. (1) Both the medial and lateral menisci act as shock absorbers and assist with load bearing of the joint. (2) The menisci work together to assist with joint congruency of the femur and tibia during motion. (3) The menisci act as secondary restraints to give the joint more stability. (4) The menisci assist with joint lubrication by helping to maintain a synovial layer inside the joint. (5) Nerve endings within the menisci are

thought to give proprioceptive feedback during motion and compression.

VIII. (1) This procedure involves taking the middle third of the patellar tendon (autograft) to replace the damaged ACL. This procedure has been referred to as the "gold standard" as it has consistently demonstrated excellent surgical outcomes with a 90 to 95% success rate in individuals returning to pre-injury levels of activity. The procedure is recommended for athletes in high-demand sports and individuals with occupations that do not require large amounts of kneeling or squatting. This procedure may not be indicated for people with a history of patellofemoral pain, arthritis, or patellar tendinitis, or for smaller individuals with a narrow patellar tendon. (2) With this procedure, the surgeon typically harvests strands of tendons from the medial semitendinosus to reconstruct the ACL. Surgeons also use additional tendons from the gracilis muscle, which creates a combined four-strand tendon graft. This procedure may be especially beneficial for younger patients who still have open growth plates. With the hamstring tendon graft, there are no graft bone ends that could violate the growth plate and stimulate early closure, as may occur with a patellar graft. (3) Surgeons also use cadaveric or allograft grafts from the Achilles tendon, tibialis anterior, and patellar tendon to replace the torn ACL. This procedure may be beneficial for patients who have failed prior ACL reconstruction or who have multiple ligaments that need repair. Advantages include decreased morbidity at the donor site, decreased surgical time, and less postoperative pain.

IX. The acronym PRICE—protection, restricted activity, ice, compression, and elevation— describes a safe early intervention strategy for an acute ankle sprain. Protection includes protecting the injured ankle with the use of crutches and appropriate ankle bracing. Restricted activity includes limiting weightbearing activity until the client is cleared by the physician. Ice should be applied every two hours for 10 to 15 minutes. Compression can be done by applying an elastic wrap to the area. This helps to minimize local swelling. Elevating the ankle 6 to 10 inches above the level of the heart will also help to control swelling. This is done to reduce hemorrhage, inflammation, swelling, and pain.

Chapter 19

Musculoskeletal Injuries of the Upper Extremity

Expand Your Knowledge

I. (1) (a) Injuries to the acromioclavicular joint can present as either traumatic or chronic. The most common mechanism of injury is a direct force on the point of the shoulder or a fall on an outstretched arm. If the clavicle does not fracture, the acromion is driven inferiorly and medially in relation to the clavicle. The ligaments are then stretched or torn, depending on the severity of the injury. This injury is often referred to as a "separated shoulder" and occurs commonly in contact sports such as football, hockey, lacrosse, and rugby. (b) Individuals with acromioclavicular joint pathology often present with pain during passive horizontal adduction or have pain during an O'Brien active compression test, which consists of resistance of the shoulder in flexion, internal rotation, and horizontal adduction. More severe cases will present with a "step-off" deformity where the separation of the clavicle and the acromion can be seen. (c) Traction through the shoulder joint should be avoided or minimized. Also, weights should not be carried around the gym. Resistive exercises in horizontal abduction or adduction should be avoided or minimized secondary to stress on the joint.

When performing scapula strengthening exercises, extremes of scapula retraction and protraction should be avoided. Internal and external rotation exercises for the rotator cuff are tolerated best with the arm in adduction. Overhead resistive activity, such as the military press and incline bench press, should be minimized or avoided. These activities should be initiated only when the client is asymptomatic and has a good proximal strength base. (2) (a) Shoulder instability can be a result of an acute, traumatic event such as a dislocation. The most common instability is anterior. It usually occurs during some combination of shoulder external rotation, abduction, and extension. Common mechanisms of injury are falling on an outstretched arm, planting a ski pole and falling forward, or trying to arm-tackle someone. It can also be a chronic condition that results from overuse activities, especially overhead activities such as when throwing or serving in tennis or volleyball, where the shoulder experiences various forces related to acceleration and deceleration. These powerful repetitive activities can cause excessive laxity in the capsule and ligaments that surround the shoulder joint. In addition, certain individuals are born with congenital joint laxity, which may predispose them to shoulder instability. (b) Clients with anterior shoulder instability may present with a positive apprehensive sign. That is, the client may become apprehensive about, or not allow the joint to be brought into, abduction and external rotation. (c) When initiating a strengthening program, submaximal, pain-free isometrics are performed for the rotator cuff and the deltoid to help reestablish stability of the shoulder joint. Precautions should be taken for the rotator cuff when performing internal and external rotation (IR/ER) exercises. The rotator cuff is often inflamed with a shoulder dislocation or instability. Isolated IR/ER exercises can increase the inflammation and thus reflexively inhibit the rotator cuff. As external rotation ROM improves and inflammation is reduced, isotonic IR/ER exercises may be incorporated using elastic resistance. (3) (a) Injuries of the rotator cuff may be chronic conditions or the result of trauma. Traumatic injuries are more common in the older population and are often related to a fall with an indirect force on an abducted arm. Tendinitis of the rotator cuff is very common and can be a result of repetitive overhead activities or incorrect body mechanics during weight training. Activities such as serving in tennis, swimming, and throwing can eccentrically overload the rotator cuff and cause tendinitis. Carrying and lifting heavy bags in daily life is another common mechanism of injury. In addition, excessive shoulder laxity or instability can predispose a person to this pathology by making the rotator cuff work much harder. Another common diagnosis of the rotator cuff is referred to as impingement syndrome. This refers to the impingement of the soft tissues between the humeral head and the archway that is formed by the acromion and the coracoacromial ligament. Conditions that narrow this archway, such as soft-tissue swelling, bone spurs, or arthritic changes, can predispose an individual to impingement. For some individuals, the acromion is congenitally hooked or curved in shape—as opposed to flat—which may predispose the client to an impingement syndrome as the acromion rubs on the rotator cuff. With overuse, the subacromial bursa can become swollen and inflamed, resulting in bursitis. As the tendons become inflamed, they may rub on the bone and become frayed and eventually lead to chronic rotator cuff tears, which can vary greatly in terms of size, thickness, and location. These tears may continue to get larger until surgical intervention may be required. (b) A person with a torn or inflamed rotator cuff may present with pain or weakness with resistive external rotation. Supraspinatus pathology

is often consistent with pain and/or weakness with resistive flexion with internal rotation in the plane of the scapula (i.e., the "empty can" position). In addition, passive full forward flexion (Neer test) and passive forward flexion and internal rotation (Hawkins-Kennedy test) may elicit pain. Weakness is sometimes a function of the severity of the injury, but there is a great deal of variability. Individuals with massive tears of the rotator cuff may have difficulty initiating elevation of the arm or maintaining it in an abducted position, but this is not always the case. Finally, individuals with rotator cuff pathology may describe a "painful arc" of range of motion. As they approach 90 degrees of elevation of the shoulder, they reach the impingement zone and complain of pain that then resolves as they move beyond that zone. (c) As in the case of shoulder instability, strengthening should be initiated with the scapula, especially in the case of a significantly inflamed rotator cuff. Any deviation in scapular function can have a negative effect on the shoulder and should be avoided. In other words, executing exercises with the scapula "set" is crucial. In addition, common causes of injury, such as overhead sports, military press, incline bench press, and lateral raises in the frontal plane, should be avoided. (4) (a) Lateral epicondylitis results from the repetitive tension overloading of the wrist and finger extensors that originate at the lateral epicondyle. Traditionally, the mechanism of injury takes place during the backhand of a novice tennis player who has poor mechanics. A change in the frequency of activity or a poorly fitted racquet can also contribute to injury. Tennis players who have a deficit in their proximal strength, such as in the scapula muscles or the rotator cuff, may be more susceptible to developing lateral epicondylitis. A lack of proximal stability may manifest itself further down the chain at the elbow. In addition, poor mechanics reduces the use of the lower body and core in the tennis stroke. This can result in increased stress on the elbow. "Tennis elbow" is often a misnomer, as this injury it is not always a result of tennis. Carrying heavy bags or performing manual labor, especially with the elbow in extension, can result in lateral epicondylitis. In addition, excessive computer work can lead to increased stress to the extensor tendons. (b) The overload can result in inflammation of the tendons that attach at the lateral epicondyle. In later stages, a mass may form in the tendon and even result in a tear. At the latter stages of pathology, clients will complain about activities such as shaking hands, holding a coffee cup, or carrying something with the elbow in extension. Pain is elicited with resistive wrist extension, especially with the elbow in extension and passive wrist flexion. (c) The causative activity must be eliminated or modified. For example, a client may be encouraged to avoid tennis or make ergonomic adjustments. In the gym, lifting weights is avoided or modified, depending on the severity of symptoms. Lifting weights with the elbow extended is to be avoided. A wrist splint may be used to rest the extensor mechanism. In addition, a counterforce brace may be used around the elbow to dissipate forces away from the injured site and reduce pain. (5) (a) Medial epicondylitis occurs due to an overload of the wrist flexors and forearm pronators. Golf, throwing, and swimming are common mechanisms of injury. Overuse or poor mechanics may lead to tendinitis or small tears of these muscles near the origin at the medial epicondyle. "Golfer's elbow" refers to an injury to the medial side of the right elbow (for a right-handed golfer). Novice golfers who fail to use their larger body parts and do not weight shift correctly are more susceptible. Beginners tend to throw the club down at the ball or hit too far behind the ball and put greater stress on the medial aspect of the elbow. Participating in throwing sports also tends to place a great deal of stress on the medial aspect of the elbow. (b) Clients will present with tenderness over the medial epicondyle or the proximal wrist flexors and pronator teres. Resistive wrist flexion or forearm pronation may elicit symptoms. In addition, performing high-load biceps curls often exacerbates symptoms. (c) Causative activities are modified or eliminated, golfers are encouraged to take lessons, throwing mechanics are reviewed, and swimming strokes are assessed. Proximal shoulder and scapular strength are assessed for any underlying deficits. (6) (a) Carpal tunnel syndrome occurs when the median nerve, which extends from the forearm into the hand, becomes compressed at the wrist. The carpal tunnel is formed by ligaments and bones at the base of the hand. Thickened tendons or other swelling can cause the nerve to become impinged or compressed. Some people are congenitally predisposed to this condition. However, common causes are wrist trauma, arthritis, work stress, and fluid retention. (b) Symptoms include burning, tingling, and numbness in the palm, thumb, index, and middle fingers. As the condition worsens, grip strength may be affected. (c) A change in positioning is often helpful for individuals with hand or wrist pain. When exercising, the wrist is often most comfortable in a neutral position. A good guideline is to avoid wrist flexion and extension greater than 30 degrees. In addition, avoid radial or ulnar deviation. Pain on the ulnar side of the wrist is often exacerbated by forearm pronation or supination. The grip size of exercise equipment can be adjusted. The ACE-AHFS may add padding to a piece of exercise equipment to create a larger grip. Often, a larger grip will reduce stress on the wrist, hand, or fingers. (7) (a) De Quervain's syndrome affects the two tendons that move the thumb away from the hand. Some experts believe the tendons become inflamed from overuse; however, the cause is not always clear or well-understood. (b) Symptoms may include pain and or swelling over the thumb side of the wrist. Gripping may also become difficult. When testing for this syndrome, the thumb is tightened as in a closed fist and the hand is tilted toward the ulna side (Finkelstein's test). If the syndrome is present, this position will produce pain at the wrist below the thumb. (c) A change in positioning is often helpful for individuals with hand or wrist pain. When exercising, the wrist is often most comfortable in a neutral position. A good guideline is to avoid wrist flexion and extension greater than 30 degrees. In addition, avoid radial or ulnar deviation. Pain on the ulnar side of the wrist is often exacerbated by forearm pronation or supination. The grip size of exercise equipment can be adjusted. The ACE-AHFS may add padding to a piece of exercise equipment to create a larger grip. Often, a larger grip will reduce stress on the wrist, hand, or fingers.

II. (1) When initiating strengthening, the ACE-AHFS should limit the ROM from below 90 degrees of forward flexion to neutral extension. This may be accomplished with elastic resistance or a cable column. When progressing, the lat pull-down should never be performed in the behind-the-neck position. This position places the shoulder in abduction and external rotation, thus increasing the stress on the shoulder capsule and ligaments. The pull-down should be performed in front and in a reclined position with the trunk in slight extension. The bar is pulled down to the chest. Aside from reducing the chance of injury, this position provides a greater mechanical advantage for the latissimus dorsi and the scapular retractors. (2) The ACE-AHFS must be aware that the long head of the biceps has an attachment at the labrum. One particular labral tear is referred to as a SLAP lesion (superior labrum from anterior to posterior). This injury occurs in the region where the biceps originate. If there has been any damage to the labrum,

excessive biceps activity may cause traction and exacerbate the injury. Biceps curls performed in a seated, supported position may reduce the chances of exacerbation. Also, avoiding end ranges of elbow extension may reduce the traction on the labrum. In addition, performing curls with a neutral forearm position will reduce the load on the biceps. (3) Modifications to the bench press include a mandatory "handoff" and spot. Next, shoulder position should be limited to below 90 degrees of forward flexion, 45 degrees of abduction, and neutral external rotation. These restrictions eliminate performance of the incline bench press, which would increase the stress on the capsule and ligaments. Repetitions should also be limited to avoid excessive fatigue, which can result in a loss of dynamic shoulder stability. Finally, weight machines such as a chest press, in which range of motion can be controlled, may be a safer option. (4) It is best to discourage clients with shoulder instability from performing this exercise. An effective initial strategy for the ACE-AHFS is to advise the client to substitute other exercises in its place. Those who want to continue the shoulder press must avoid the behind-the-neck position. This position places significant stress on the shoulder capsule and ligaments and places the shoulder in a relatively unstable position. Bringing the shoulder into a more anterior position or closer to the scapular plane significantly reduces the stress to the shoulder capsule and ligaments and provides better joint conformity between the humeral head and the glenoid fossa. Again, weight machines may provide a safer alternative to free weights.

III. For those with shoulder impingement syndrome who want to continue deltoid strengthening, scapular plane elevation is preferred to performing lateral raises in the frontal plane. The exercise in the scapular plane affords the least amount of stress on the shoulder. It is also a more functional plane in which to work. Finally, this exercise also recruits much of the scapula musculature, and to some extent the supraspinatus. The "empty can" position described for strengthening the supraspinatus is not advised, as the internally rotated position significantly increases the chance of shoulder impingement and is a common source of shoulder pain.

IV. Initiating a strengthening program using multijoint exercises, such as rowing, shrugs, lat pull-downs, and PNF patterns, allows some strengthening of the wrist and forearm without trying to isolate them. These exercises also provide a more global approach to strengthening the entire upper extremity and establishing proximal strength. These exercises should be performed while avoiding the end ranges of elbow extension. When a client is performing any activity, increasing the grip size of resistive equipment or a tennis racquet can reduce the amount of wrist extensor activity and the amount of stress on the lateral epicondyle.

Chapter 20

Low-back Pain

Expand Your Knowledge

I. (1) LBP occurs most commonly in the 30- to 55-year-old age group. Herniated disks are most common in those between the ages of 30 and 40, a time when the water content of intervertebral disks has decreased. The prevalence of back pain increases with age until age 60, with older individuals experiencing greater rates of chronic or intermittent pain. (2) Overall, men and women appear to be equally affected. However, older women have a higher prevalence of back pain than older men, which may be secondary to the greater rates of osteoporosis of the spine seen in women. In contrast, men are more involved in heavy work, and therefore have higher rates of occupational back pain. (3) Body weight, height, and body build have not been shown to have a strong correlation with LBP. (4) Smoking is thought to be a significant risk factor for LBP. Smoking may decrease blood flow to the intervertebral discs, leading to a deficit of nutrients and/or a lack of sufficient oxygen, which may lead to accelerated cell death. Other effects of smoking may include an increase in the rate of development of osteoporosis, fractures, and degenerative changes in the spine. In addition, chronic coughing may be an indirect link between smoking and back pain. (5) Certain types of occupational activities appear to predispose individuals to LBP, including heavy lifting, carrying, pulling, pushing, prolonged walking or standing, driving, and working night shifts. High exposure to whole-body vibration is also a risk factor for back pain. Specific professions that are at higher risk include sales, clerical work, repair service, and transportation. Work-related stress and dissatisfaction are also associated with the development of LBP. (6) Athletes involved in certain activities, such as cross-country skiing and rowing, may have higher rates of LBP than non-athletes. In general, those who engage in regular recreational physical activity appear to be less likely to have back pain at any given time and are less likely to develop future pain. However, some high-intensity or repetitive exercises (i.e., golf and tennis) may predispose or worsen an existing condition. While physical fitness does not completely prevent LBP, it may improve functional outcomes by decreasing recovery time. (7) Chronic back pain sufferers are six times more likely to be depressed than individuals without pain. Depression may affect an individual's ability to cope with pain. The inability to determine an exact cause of pain or to effectively relieve symptoms may result in further depression.

II. (a) 80%; (b) 97%; 2%; 1%; (c) Discogenic back pain; (d) herniated disc; (e) radiculopathy; (f) spinal stenosis; (g) pars interarticularis; an anterior displacement of a vertebra relative to the one below it

III. (1) Trigger point injections target areas of muscle that are painful and fail to relax. (2) Facet injections target facet joints on the posterior aspect of the spine that form where one vertebra overlaps another. Pain from facet joints can cause localized spinal pain or refer pain to adjacent structures. (3) Epidural injections target the epidural space inside the spinal canal that contains, among other structures, spinal nerve roots. This may help decrease pain and inflammation of these structures and their associated structures.

IV. (1) The theoretical goals of flexion exercises are to open the intervertebral foramina and facet joints, strengthen the abdominal muscles, and stretch the back extensors. (2) Extension exercises aim to improve motor coordination, strengthen the back extensors, improve mobility, and, perhaps, shift disrupted nuclear material to a more normal position. (3) Isometric stabilization exercises promote abdominal strength and co-contraction of trunk muscles by a series of moves that ultimately result in a posterior pelvic tilt.

V. (1) Centralization occurs when active motion of the lumbar spine causes symptoms to either resolve or move from the periphery to the lumbar spine. Symptoms most commonly localize with either flexion, usually in individuals with degenerative or stenotic conditions, or extension, usually in individuals with lumbar disc herniation. For these individuals, the rehabilitation program can focus on exercises using the centralizing movement (either flexion or extension) with the goals of decreasing the severity of symptoms and increasing activity level. (2) In lumbar stabilization, the goals of treatment are to further increase activity level and decrease disability. Exercises focus on the muscles that provide support and stabilization of the lumbar spine: transverse abdominis, erector spinae, multifidus, quadratus lumborum, and oblique abdominals. While each muscle has a specific function, they all work in concert to stabilize the lumbar spine during everyday activities. (3) Clients progress to dynamic stabilization after developing core strength and endurance. The goals of dynamic stabilization therapy are to return the client to full activity. Exercises in this stage are performed on an unstable surface such as a stability ball. Exercises can progress through balancing on a ball while performing upper- and lower-extremity movements holding weights to standing exercises incorporating a trampoline, wobble board, or foam roller. In this stage, clients are reminded to engage their core muscles to maintain spinal stability while performing all dynamic exercises.

VI. (1) Clients should be encouraged to obtain clearance from their physicians before beginning a program, as exercise may not be appropriate for certain individuals with serious conditions such as tumor, fracture, or progressive neurologic deficits. (2) Although walking is generally a good choice for aerobic fitness in clients with LBP because it places low compressive loads on the lumbar structures, it may not be suitable for all clients. Because walking places the lumbar spine in a more extended position, clients with spinal stenosis who have symptoms while walking that are relieved with rest, should avoid prolonged walking. (3) The progression of exercises can be as important as the exercises themselves. In general, the ACE-AHFS should consider working on the muscles that stabilize the spine prior to the muscles that move the spine, to decrease the likelihood that unsupported exercises will cause damage to ligaments. (4) Clients in beginning stages may not need additional weight added to exercises.

Initially, the weight of their limbs may provide enough of a challenge. (5) Know each client's limitations as set forth by his or her physician or physical therapist prior to designing the exercise program. Avoid extreme postures or actions that take the individual beyond his or her normal range of motion. (6) Respect the client's normal spinal curvature when performing trunk exercises. Avoid hyperextension of the spine, which would cause clients to exceed their normal lordosis. (7) Many of the exercises used in LBP rehabilitation require only subtle movements, such as abdominal hollowing. Using extreme movements or momentum is usually unwarranted for individuals with a history of LBP. (8) Although a hands-on approach can be beneficial to provide adjustments and guidance, the ACE-AHFS must never physically force a client into a position. Providing extra force to bring a client "deeper" into a stretch can cause serious injury.

VII. Many people hurt their backs in an attempt to increase strength. Some exercise programs intended to enhance strength contain poorly chosen exercises such as sit-ups. Performing sit-ups both replicates a potent injury mechanism (i.e., posterior disc herniation) and results in high loads on the spine. On the other hand, muscle endurance, as opposed to strength, has been shown to be protective against future back troubles. Further, for many people, it is better to train for stability rather than stretch to increase range of motion. Investigations into injury mechanisms have revealed that many back-training practices actually replicate the loads and motions that cause parts of the low back to become injured.

VIII. Diurnal variation in the fluid level of the intervertebral discs (i.e., discs are more hydrated early in the morning after rising from bed) changes the stresses on the discs throughout the day. Specifically, they are highest following bed rest and

diminish over the subsequent few hours. Therefore, it would be very unwise to perform full-range spine motion while under load shortly after rising from bed.

IX. (1) Groove motion/motor patterns, and corrective exercise; (2) Build whole-body and joint stability; (3) Increase muscle endurance; (4) Build muscle strength; (5) Develop power and agility

X. The "crossed-pelvis syndrome" is a phenomenon that occurs when the gluteal complex is inhibited during squatting patterns. It is very common in individuals with a history of back problems. Individuals with impaired gluteal motor patterns are unable to spare their backs during squatting patterns since they rely on their hamstrings and erector spinae to drive the extension motion. In turn, the erector spinae forces create loads that compress the lumbar spine. It is impossible to achieve optimal squat performance without well-integrated hip extensor or gluteal patterns. Retraining of the gluteals cannot be achieved with conventional barbell squat exercises. Performing a conventional squat requires relatively little hip abduction. As a result, gluteus medius activation is minimized and activation of the gluteus maximus is delayed during the traditional barbell squat until lower squat angles are reached. The barbell squat is primarily a quadriceps exercise and not a gluteal exercise in the truest sense. Unlike the conventional barbell squat, the single-leg squat elicits almost immediate activation of the gluteus medius and more rapid integration of the gluteus maximus during the squat descent to assist in the frontal plane hip drive needed for common activities such as running and jumping.

XI. (1) Develop general fitness and balancing ability to train safely and effectively. (2) Consider the matching of a client's fitness level and motor abilities to the skill demands of the planned training program. (3) Develop the foundation of proper motor and motion patterns to protect any potential weak links. (4) Consider the balance of strength around a joint and between adjacent joints, as well as the balance of strength to endurance. (5) Consider the range of motion required by the task and whether the client's motion capability is appropriately matched.

Chapter 21

Older Adults

Expand Your Knowledge

I. (1) The maximum number of years an organism from a given species can live is called its lifespan. Lifespan is different from life expectancy, which is the average number of years a person can expect to live. (2) Chronological age is a quantitative representation of the length of time a person has lived since birth. Functional age takes into account a person's biological, psychological, and social characteristics to create a picture of aging as whole. (3) Residual volume is the volume of air remaining in the lungs at the end of maximal expiration, whereas expiratory reserve volume is the maximal volume of air that can be expelled from the lungs after normal expiration. (4) Muscle atrophy is a general term used to describe a loss of muscle tissue. Muscle atrophy that occurs as a natural part of the aging process is called sarcopenia and reflects both a decrease in the average fiber size and a decrease in the number of muscle fibers. (5) Neuromuscular coordination is defined as the ability to activate large and small muscles with the correct amount of force in the most efficient sequence to accomplish a task. A specific type of neuromuscular coordination called hand-eye coordination is defined as the "skillful, integrated use of the eyes, arms, hands, and fingers in fine, precision movement."

II. The reasons for the age-related decline in maximum heart rate could include alterations in catecholamine response and increased stiffness of the heart wall. Epinephrine and norepinephrine (catecholamines), which act through the sympathetic nervous system, increase the contractility of the heart muscle. With aging, the heart and blood vessels become less sensitive to catecholamine stimulation. Thus, the aging heart cannot achieve the maximum heart rate levels that were possible during youth.

III. (1) A reduction in maximum heart rate with advancing age; (2) Decreases in muscle tissue and its ability to use oxygen; (3) A diminished ability to redirect blood flow from organs to working muscles

IV. As muscle fibers atrophy, they are replaced by fatty and fibrous (collagen) tissue. Collagen is a primary component of connective tissue that exhibits a low compliance, which contributes to the stiffening and decreased mobility of aging muscle. Additionally, a significant loss (up to 15%) of body water between the ages of 30 and 80 contributes to increased stiffness in soft tissues. Collectively, these changes appear to be partly responsible for flexibility loss due to aging. However, it is possible that the reduction in ROM is due, in part, to lack of physical activity, since there is some evidence that not all older adults lose flexibility at the same rate.

V. Short-term memory decreases with age, which limits the ability to develop new skills and concepts. Providing written instructions, allowing an extended time period for the anticipation of performing a new task, and prolonging the inspection period of learning a new task may enhance the learning experience for an older adult.

VI. (1) Anticipation is helpful for older adults, as they plan their movements for selected tasks well before the task is performed. When the time comes to initiate the task, such as grabbing a suitcase off of a luggage carousel at the airport, the older person has had time to anticipate the upcoming required movements so that they can be made quickly and efficiently. (2) Simplification is used by older adults to compensate for losses in coordination by making complex movements less complicated. Breaking movements into simpler tasks to achieve the same end result compensates for the decline in coordination. For example, older people may sit on a stool to pull weeds from a garden, whereas younger people bend over and stand up many times while performing the same chore. (3) Choosing accuracy over speed is another tactic that helps compensate for decreased coordination. By choosing to move slower, older subjects allow more time for visual and proprioceptive feedback to detect and correct errors, which could help explain the tendency for older adults to move slower and proceed more cautiously while performing physical tasks than younger adults.

VII. Postural sway is functionally significant because it is related to the risk of falling—specifically for older people who fall without warning and without a loss of consciousness, as opposed to those who trip and fall. This aspect of static balance is of interest because it may identify individuals at a higher risk for falling, and for whom behavioral and physiological strategies can be developed and implemented to help prevent falls.

VIII. (1) Throughout the aging process, vision becomes degraded and provides decreased or distorted information. As a result, poor visual acuity is associated with an increased number of falls in the elderly. With aging, most individuals lose the ability to detect the spatial information that is important for balance. These changes impair the quality of visual input received and will result in slower processing of the incoming sensory feedback, poor integration of sensory inputs, and an altered kinesthetic awareness. Consequently, an older adult's

ability to avoid obstacles, negotiate terrain, and efficiently move about in low-light conditions will be negatively affected. (2) The process of aging brings about a decline in an individual's ability to sense cutaneous inputs, which results in a reduced ability to feel the quality of contact between the feet and the supporting surface. Additionally, muscle spindle activity and, to a lesser degree, joint receptor inputs are impaired with aging. (3) As early as age 30, hair cells within the vestibular system begin to decline in density, resulting in a reduced sensitivity to head movements. Individuals over age 70 may have lost 40% of the sensory cells within the vestibular system. Consequently, an increase in sway and in the risk of falling are likely, especially when the visual and the somatosensory systems are impaired. Decreases in vestibular function also have been associated with visual problems and dizziness in older adults.

IX. (1) One explanation for the decreased gait-related function in the elderly is the theory of motion economy. Locomotion requires the expenditure of energy. Researchers theorize that in both humans and animals, gait speeds are chosen that are most economical in terms of energy consumption. Humans, presumably, prefer certain speeds of walking because those speeds are the most economical for them based on their body structure, weight, muscular strength, and flexibility. Therefore, older walkers may use the strategy of increasing stride frequency instead of stride length because it maximizes their motion economy. Furthermore, the endurance of weaker lower-body muscles is maximized with shorter strides, and the energy cost of walking is minimized. (2) Another possible explanation is that slower gait speeds allow older adults to spend more time monitoring the progress and result of walking and to respond to changes in the environment. Additionally, limited ranges of motion in the ankles and knees are responsible for a shortened stride length. Lastly, a decreased ability to balance encourages older individuals to spend less time in the single-support phase of gait, and the increased time spent in double-support ultimately slows gait speed.

X. (1) Decreased lean mass and increased body fat; (2) Reduction in total body water; (3) Decreased efficiency of the gastrointestinal tract; (4) Decreased cardiac output; (5) Decreased efficiency of the liver and kidneys

XI. (1) The Berg Balance Scale evaluates an individual's ability to perform a series of functional tasks that require balance. Many of the tasks simulate activities likely to be encountered by older adults in their daily lives, such as transfers, object retrieval, and turning. The BBS also may be used for identifying older adults who need intervention in the way of a comprehensive functional balance-training program. The BBS is recommended for assessing lower-functioning older adults. (2) The Fullerton Advanced Balance Scale (FAB) is designed to measure changes in balance occurring in higher-functioning older adults. Therefore, it is appropriate for use with community-dwelling older adults who are most likely to enroll in a community-based fitness program. The FAB Scale consists of 10 items that include a combination of static and dynamic balance activities performed in different sensory environments, as well as items that may help identify those at risk for falling as a result of sensory impairments. The FAB Scale was created for use as an alternative to the BBS, as the BBS tends to produce a ceiling effect (i.e., very high scores on repeated tests) when administered to higher-functioning older adults with impaired balance.

XII. Aquatic exercise can help older clients develop confidence and minimize the fears and risks associated with falling. The water's buoyancy provides support, while the water's resistance provides a medium in which to perform exercise movements slowly so that clients can rehearse balance-recovery patterns in a safe environment. In other words, balance training in a pool, where water can support a stumble or fall, allows clients to make movement errors safely and practice corrections with more confidence. Water's buoyancy and viscosity slow down a client's movements, thereby lowering the risk of injury. Water's resistive properties also provide a natural overload for muscular conditioning. As movement speed in the water increases, resistance increases and is proportional to the effort applied. For the maximum balance benefit, muscular conditioning should target the core, legs, and ankles through functional ranges of motion. Combining speed and strength to work on power, especially for the lower body, can help improve quick recovery when clients lose their balance during the course of their daily activities.

XIII. (1) Clients should keep fingernails trimmed to avoid puncturing the elastic and prevent discomfort while holding the band or tube. (2) They should remove jewelry prior to exercise. (3) The ACE-AHFS should check bands and tubing for wear, tears, and rubbing before use, and replace as needed. (4) The ACE-AHFS should check connections and secure attachments prior to each use. (5) Clients must protect the eyes during exercise. (6) Clients should avoid stretching the band or tubing to more than 300% elongation to prevent breakage. (7) Persons with latex allergies should use latex-free forms of elastic resistance.

XIV. (1) With age, the amount of ascorbic acid produced in the stomach, which helps absorb vitamin B12, decreases. To avoid deficiency, older adults are advised to regularly eat foods rich in vitamin B12, including meat, poultry, fish, eggs, and dairy foods. To get the recommended intake of vitamin B12, older adults may need to take a dietary supplement. However, they should discuss supplementation with their physician. (2) Vitamin C deficiencies are linked to an inability to buy expensively priced fresh fruits and vegetables. It is important for older adults to enjoy a wide variety of foods. Eating nutrient-dense foods becomes increasingly important when calorie needs decline but vitamin and mineral needs remain high. (3) Deficiencies in vitamin D are attributed to the limited exposure of older people to sunlight. Eating nutrient-dense foods becomes increasingly important when calorie needs decline but vitamin and mineral needs remain high. To get the recommended IU of vitamin D, older adults may need to take a dietary supplement. However, they should discuss supplementation with their physician. (4) A lack of vitamin D, in turn, diminishes the absorption of calcium and increases the risk of developing osteoporosis. Calcium intake of many older people falls below the level recommended for protection from osteoporosis. Furthermore, the prolonged administration of antacids may increase calcium loss in the stool. Eating nutrient-dense foods becomes increasingly important when calorie needs decline but vitamin and mineral needs remain high. To get the recommended intake of calcium, older adults may need to take a dietary supplement. However, they should discuss supplementation with their physician. (5) A reduced gastric secretion

of hydrochloric acid and enzymes may restrict the absorption of iron, which could result in anemia. Antacid use also interferes with iron absorption. Furthermore, medications that cause blood loss, such as anticoagulants, aspirin, and arthritis drugs, can lead to a tendency toward anemia. Iron absorption may be improved by eating iron-rich foods with vitamin C–rich fruits and vegetables. (6) Zinc deficiencies are common in older people. As many as 95% of older adults may not get the zinc they need, and zinc absorption also may be less efficient in this population. Zinc deficiency, in turn, may lead to a depressed appetite and a diminished sense of taste, which may lead to lower food intakes and worsened zinc status. Regular consumption of meats, eggs, and seafood should provide adequate zinc intake.

XV. (1) A narrower base to reflect the lower energy needs of older adults; (2) Replacement of selected food icons with nutrient-dense examples to help reconcile decreased food intake with unchanged or increased recommended dietary allowances; (3) Addition of a fiber icon in appropriate food categories to facilitate achieving adequate intakes to promote optimal bowel function; (4) Inclusion of a row of glasses at the base of the pyramid to remind older adults to maintain adequate fluid intakes; (5) Placement of a flag at the top to alert some older adults that their healthcare providers should consider recommending vitamins B12 or D or calcium supplements

Chapter 22

Youth

Expand Your Knowledge

I. (a) six and 17; (b) 61%; 33%; (c) doubled; tripled; (d) 45%; (e) carried into adulthood;

(f) puberty; eight and 13; nine and 15; (g) tidal volume; (h) stroke volumes

II. (1) Enhanced muscular fitness; (2) Increased bone mineral density; (3) Improved body composition; (4) Improved motor fitness performance; (5) Enhanced sports performance; (6) Increased resistance to injury; (7) Enhanced psychological well-being; (8) Improved attitude toward lifelong physical activity; (9) Enhanced academic performance

III. Unlike adults, who tend to specialize in such sports as weightlifting and long-distance running, the strongest child in a class is likely to be a leader in an endurance run as well. These observations are supported by laboratory data that suggest that children with a high maximal oxygen uptake tend to perform well during anaerobic tests. The ACE-AHFS should appreciate the lack of metabolic specialization in children, and therefore expose youth to a variety of sports and activities during this developmental period.

IV. When evaluating youth, it is important to avoid the "pass-fail" mentality, as this approach may actually discourage unfit or overweight boys and girls from participating in fitness classes or other physical-activity programs. To create an environment in which boys and girls enjoy the fitness assessment and feel good about participating, the ACE-AHFS should not refer to the assessment as a test, but instead call it a "challenge." As such, fitness assessments should provide youth with an opportunity to demonstrate what they can do now that they could not do before.

V. The ACE-AHFS should focus on the accumulation of physical activity throughout the day rather than on continuous bouts of physical activity performed at a predetermined intensity. While continuous moderate-to-vigorous physical activity is not physiologically harmful, it is not the most appropriate method of exercise for youth, who tend to enjoy non-sustained

activities or games. In fact, continuous moderate-to-vigorous physical activity lasting more than five to 10 minutes without rest or recovery is rare among children, because they relatively have short attention spans and do not enjoy this type of training. Therefore, the ACE-AHFS should assess the needs and abilities of all participants, and carefully design physical-activity programs that alternate moderate-to-vigorous amounts of physical activity with brief periods of rest and recovery as needed.

VI. (1) Begin with 20 to 30 minutes of intermittent aerobic exercise. (2) Gradually progress to 60 minutes or more on all or most days of the week. (3) Alternate moderate and vigorous bouts of aerobic exercise with brief rest periods. (4) Estimate exercise intensity by simple observation. (5) Participate in a variety of developmentally appropriate aerobic activities that include locomotion skills and apparatus activities. (6) Perform aerobic activities that are challenging, interesting, and fun.

VII. (1) Start with one or two sets of 10 to 15 repetitions using light to moderate loads. (2) Increase the resistance gradually (5 to 10%) as strength improves. (3) Emphasize correct exercise technique instead of the amount of weight lifted. (4) Progress to multiple sets of six to 15 repetitions on selected exercises. (5) Progress from simple to more advanced movements that require balance and coordination. (6) Strength train two to three times per week on nonconsecutive days. (7) Use individualized workout logs to monitor progress. (8) Cool down with less intense activities and static stretching.

VIII. A dynamic warm-up for youth may include low-, moderate-, and high-intensity hops, skips, and jumps, as well as various movement-based exercises for the upper and lower body.

In addition to the physiological value, these movements satisfy the need for children to move at the start of each session, which also helps focus their attention on listening and learning. The ACE-AHFS should begin each session with a 10- to 15-minute period of 10 to 12 drills (e.g., high-knee marches, lateral shuffles) that progress from low to higher intensity. Participants should perform each dynamic movement for about 10 yards, rest for five to 10 seconds, and then repeat the same exercise for 10 yards as they return to the starting point.

IX. A traditional anatomical concern associated with youth fitness programs involves the potential for injury to the epiphysis, or growth plate, of children's long bones. Although injury to the growth plate is a serious concern, this type of injury seems to be largely preventable if the volume and intensity of exercise are carefully programmed and children are taught how to perform exercises properly. Traditional concerns involving the potential for injury to immature skeletons are being replaced with scientific findings that suggest that appropriate weightbearing physical activity is actually a potent stimulus for bone mineralization in children.

X. (1) Keep instructions short and simple. Even the best fitness activities will not work if participants do not understand the rules. (2) Avoid using vague terms and realize that the choice of words can influence a child's ability to understand what was said. The use of "show and tell" demonstrations can assist in explaining an exercise or game. (3) If the element of fun seems to be missing, reevaluate the intellectual requirements of the game or activity.

XI. (1) Encourage youngsters to eat breakfast. A well-balanced meal at the start of the day can enhance cognitive performance and provide energy. (2) Provide healthy "grab-and-go" foods such as raisins, air-popped popcorn, and low-fat yogurt at health clubs and recreation centers. (3) Create games and fun activities that encourage healthy eating habits and invite parents to be part of the nutrition education program so they can plan healthy meals and keep healthy snacks at home. (4) Give children and teenagers healthy snack ideas, such as baby carrots with low-fat dressing and celery sticks with peanut butter. (5) Set a good example by choosing healthy snacks before and after class. If youngsters see adults eating high-fat snacks, they will likely imitate the behavior.

XII. Children and teenagers should be encouraged to drink water before, during, and after every fitness class. Although a decrease in body weight of only 1% through exercise-induced sweating negatively affects performance, dehydration levels of 2 to 3% or even higher are commonly reported in youth sports. Because youth respond to dehydration with an excessive increase in body core temperature and a greater risk of heat-related illnesses, the ACE-AHFS should make every effort to ensure that youth arrive fully hydrated and drink fluid before, during, and after the exercise session or sports competition. Although plain water is adequate for activities lasting less than one hour, some boys and girls may find sports drinks more palatable than water. If a youngster prefers the taste of flavored drinks, he or she may be more likely to drink regularly and avoid voluntary dehydration.

Chapter 23

Pre- and Postnatal Exercise

Expand Your Knowledge

I. (1) Preliminary studies have found that women who participated in any type of recreational activity within the first 20 weeks of gestation decreased their risk of GDM by almost half. Research has shown that even mild exercise (30% of $\dot{V}O_2$max, regardless of modality) combined with nutritional control can help prevent GDM and excessive weight gain during pregnancy. (2) Regular leisure-time physical activity in early pregnancy is associated with a reduced incidence of preeclampsia. Although not proven, several protective mechanisms associated with exercise are thought to play a role in preeclampsia prevention, including enhanced placental growth and vascularity, enhanced antioxidant defense systems, reduction of the systemic inflammatory response, and improved endothelial function. (3) Regular aerobic exercise and educational seminars on restoring fertility in obese women have been shown to be effective. The subjects who completed such intervention lost an average of 22.4 ± 9.5 lb (10.1 ± 4.3 kg). The authors hypothesized that improved fertility resulted from the beneficial effects of reduced insulin resistance and lower insulin concentrations on reproductive hormone profiles. Exercise performed before conception and during pregnancy may help to prevent obesity-related complications by decreasing BMI to a healthy range, preventing GDM and preeclampsia, and reducing the likelihood of excessive gestational weight gain. Prenatal exercise also has been associated with a timely return to pre-pregnancy weight after delivery.

II. (1) The selective redistribution of blood flow away from the fetus during regular or prolonged exercise in pregnancy may interfere with the transplacental transport of oxygen, carbon dioxide, and nutrients. To address this concern, many experts recommend aquatic exercise as an excellent choice of aerobic training during pregnancy. During immersion, women experience a smaller decrease in plasma volume as compared to exercising on land. In addition, as a result of the hydrostatic pressure in aquatic exercise, maintenance of blood flow around the central organs may provide better maintenance of uterine and placental blood flow. (2) During exercise, transient hypoxia could result in fetal tachycardia and an increase in fetal blood pressure. These fetal responses are protective mechanisms that occur during obstetric events and allow the fetus to facilitate the transfer of oxygen and decrease the carbon dioxide tension across the placenta. However, there are no reports to link such adverse events with maternal exercise. A majority of studies examining fetal responses to exercise monitored fetal heart rate as an indicator of fetal stress. Most of these studies show a minimum or moderate increase in fetal heart rate by 10 to 30 beats per minute over baseline during or after maternal exercise. (3) This is another theoretical concern related to strenuous physical activity. Studies on the effect of exercise during pregnancy and resultant birth weights are inconclusive. Epidemiological studies have shown a link between strenuous physical activity, poor diet, and low birth weight. It has also been reported that mothers who perform strenuous physical work in their occupations, such as repetitive lifting, have a tendency to deliver earlier and have small-for-gestational-age infants. However, other studies have provided conflicting data suggesting that other variables, such as inefficient nutrition, have to be present for strenuous activities to affect fetal growth. Overall, it appears that birth weight is not affected by exercise in women who have adequate energy intake.

III. By mid-pregnancy, cardiac outputs are 30 to 50% greater than before pregnancy. Additionally, maternal stroke volume increases by 10% by the end of the first trimester, and is followed by a 20% increase in heart rate during the second and third trimesters. Maternal resting heart rate can be up to 15 beats per minute higher than pre-pregnancy rates near the third trimester.

Mean arterial pressure decreases by 5 to 10 mmHg by the middle of the second trimester before gradually increasing back to pre-pregnancy levels. These hemodynamic changes appear to establish a circulatory reserve necessary to provide nutrients and oxygen to both mother and fetus at rest and during moderate exercise.

IV. Prenatal adaptations of the respiratory system cause women to experience an associated increase in oxygen uptake and a 10 to 20% increase in baseline oxygen consumption. Peak ventilation and maximal aerobic capacity are maintained during pregnancy. As a result of this maintained function and the pregnancy-induced increase in alveolar ventilation, gas transfer at the tissue level may improve. This causes a "training effect" of pregnancy in women who maintain moderate-to-intense exercise programs throughout gestation, and may explain anecdotal reports of women who experience an improvement in competitive endurance performance after giving birth.

V. During moderate-intensity aerobic exercise in thermoneutral conditions, the core temperature of non-pregnant women rises an average of 1.5° C during the first 30 minutes of exercise, and then reaches a plateau if exercise is continued for an additional 30 minutes. If heat production exceeds heat dissipation capacity, as is commonly the case during exercise in hot, humid conditions or during very high-intensity exercise, a woman's core temperature will continue to rise. During prolonged exercise, loss of fluid as sweat may compromise heat dissipation. Given that fetal body core temperatures are naturally about 1° C higher than maternal temperatures, maintenance of proper hydration, and therefore blood volume, is critical to heat balance.

VI. (1) Consuming additional calories to maintain homeostasis; (2) Avoiding motionless standing; (3) Preventing maternal hyperthermia; (4) Preventing maternal hypoglycemia; (5) Avoiding high-risk exercises

VII. (1) All women without contraindications should be encouraged to participate in aerobic and strength-conditioning exercises as part of a healthy lifestyle during their pregnancy. (2) Reasonable goals of aerobic conditioning in pregnancy should be to maintain a good fitness level throughout pregnancy without trying to reach peak fitness or train for an athletic competition. (3) Women should choose activities that will minimize the risk of loss of balance and fetal trauma. (4) Women should be advised that adverse pregnancy or neonatal outcomes are not increased for exercising women. (5) Initiation of pelvic floor exercises in the immediate postpartum period may reduce the risk of future urinary incontinence. (6) Women should be advised that moderate exercise during lactation does not affect the quantity or composition of breast milk or impact infant growth.

VIII. To alleviate the postural discomforts of exercise, many pregnant women choose to work out in the water. Women who participate in an aquatic exercise class have been shown to experience reduced symptoms of back pain during late pregnancy and miss fewer days at work compared to a control group. Aquatic exercise in relatively cool water decreases the rise in body temperature observed during land-based exercise, which can help minimize the risk of hyperthermia. The hydrostatic pressure exerted on a pregnant woman's body during pool exercise may lessen fluid retention and swelling, and the buoyancy of water supports the bodyweight, relieving pressure on the weightbearing joints and allowing the muscles relief from bearing extra mechanical stress during the pregnancy. Thus, aquatic exercise is a valuable option for women to consider, especially as advancing pregnancy makes other forms of physical activity uncomfortable or stressful on the joints.

IX. The hypothetical origins of sacroiliac (SI) joint dysfunction during pregnancy focus on decreased stability of the pelvic girdle. It is assumed that the stability of the pelvic girdle is provided, in part, by the coarse texture of the SI cartilage surfaces, the undulated shape of the joint, and the compressive forces of the muscles, ligaments, and thoracolumbar fascia. Muscles that generate a force perpendicular to the SI joints or increase tension on the sacroiliac ligaments or thoracolumbar fascia generate forces that may act to stabilize the SI joint. These include the internal and external abdominal obliques, the latissimus dorsi, the transversospinal parts of the erector spinae muscle (especially the multifidus), and the gluteus maximus. Therefore, functional exercise programs that target this musculature may benefit women with prenatal pelvic pain, partly by increasing muscle force and endurance.

X. Diastasis recti is a partial or complete separation between the left and right sides of the rectus abdominis muscle. During pregnancy, the maternal inferior thoracic diameter is increased, thus altering the spatial relationship between the superior and inferior abdominal muscle attachments. In addition, anterior and lateral dimensions of the abdomen during pregnancy increase the distance between muscle attachments, producing increases in muscle length. In some women, the rectus abdominis muscles move laterally and may remain separated in the immediate post-delivery period.

XI. (1) Multiple pregnancies; (2) Vaginal delivery; (3) High infant birth weight; (4) Large infant cranial circumference; (5) High maternal weight gain during pregnancy; (6) Tearing of the perineum during delivery

XII. (1) Providing support for the pelvic organs; (2) Preventing prolapse of the bladder, uterus, and rectum; (3) Supporting proper pelvic alignment; (4) Reinforcing sphincter control; (5) Enhancing circulation to the pelvic floor muscles; (6) Providing a healthy environment for the healing process after labor and delivery

XIII. A disorder related to postpartum depression, but considered not as severe, is called "maternity blues." Maternity blues refers to the tearfulness, irritability, hypochondriasis, sleeplessness, impairment of concentration, and headache that occurs in the 10 days or so postpartum. A peak in symptoms typically occurs around the fourth to fifth day after delivery, coinciding with maximal hormonal changes, which include falling concentrations of progesterone, estradiol, and cortisol and rising prolactin concentrations. During pregnancy, progesterone concentrations slowly rise to a maximum until they reach levels several hundred times higher than normal. After delivery and the withdrawal of the placenta, there is a precipitous drop in progesterone concentration. It is hypothesized that the symptoms of maternity blues are related to progesterone withdrawal. Cortisol concentrations also rise during pregnancy to several times their normal values. They rise further during the stress of labor and then slowly return to normal within 15 days of delivery.

XIV. (1) Preventing obesity (or overweight) through promotion of body fat/body weight loss; (2) Promoting aerobic fitness and strength, leading to an improved ability to perform activities of mothering; (3) Optimizing bone health by increasing bone mineral density and/or preventing lactation-associated bone loss; (4) Improving mood or self-esteem

XV. Training the pelvic-floor musculature goes hand-in-hand with performing exercises to strengthen the core. Research findings have shown that maximum pelvic-floor muscle contractions are not possible without a co-contraction of the abdominal muscles, specifically the transverse abdominis and internal oblique muscles. This abdominal contraction can be observed as a small inward movement of the lower abdomen. Prior to any strenuous abdominal exercise, postnatal clients should perform transverse abdominis work (i.e., a drawing-in maneuver), pelvic tilts, and spinal stabilization exercises. Since traditional abdominal crunches compress the abdominal space and increase pressure on the pelvic floor, they should be reserved for exercise regimens after the postnatal client has had time to re-educate the pelvic floor muscles through Kegel training and core stabilization work.